The 12 Key Pillars of Novel Construction
WORKBOOK

Your Blueprint for Building a Solid Story

By C. S. Lakin

The Writer's Toolbox Series

The 12 Key Pillars of Novel Construction Workbook by C. S. Lakin

ISBN-10: 0991389484

ISBN-13: 978-0-9913894-8-3

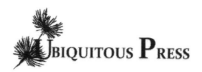

UBIQUITOUS PRESS

Ubiquitous Press

Morgan Hill, CA

Books by C. S. Lakin

Writing Craft

The 12 Key Pillars of Novel Construction: Your Blueprint for Building a Solid Story

Shoot Your Novel: Cinematic Techniques to Supercharge Your Writing

Writing the Heart of Your Story: The Secret to Crafting an Unforgettable Novel

Say What? The Fiction Writer's Handy Guide to Grammar, Punctuation, and Word Usage

Novels

Someone to Blame

Conundrum

Innocent Little Crimes

A Thin Film of Lies

Intended for Harm

The Wolf of Tebron

The Map across Time

The Land of Darkness

The Unraveling of Wentwater

The Crystal Scepter

The Sands of Ethryn

The Hidden Kingdom

Time Sniffers

Writing as Charlene Whitman

Colorado Promise

Colorado Hope

Table of Contents

INTRODUCTION...1

HOW TO USE THIS WORKBOOK 4

THE FOUR CORNER PILLARS 6

   PILLAR #1: CONCEPT WITH A KICKER 7

      Inspection Checklist #1 27

   PILLAR #2: PROTAGONIST WITH A GOAL 44

      Inspection Checklist #2 54

   PILLAR #3: CONFLICT WITH HIGH STAKES 68

      Inspection Checklist #3 79

   PILLAR #4: THEME WITH A HEART 96

      Inspection Checklist #4 110

THE EIGHT SUPPORTING PILLARS...126

   PILLAR #5: PLOT AND SUBPLOTS IN A STRING OF SCENES 127

      Inspection Checklist #5 154

   PILLAR #6: SECONDARY CHARACTERS 168

      Inspection Checklist #6 178

   PILLAR #7: SETTING WITH A PURPOSE 190

      Inspection Checklist #7 200

   PILLAR #8: TENSION RAMPED TO THE MAX 212

   PILLAR #9: DIALOG—COMPRESSED AND ESSENTIAL..............................230

   PILLAR #10: VOICE—UNIQUE FOR EACH CHARACTER.............................241

      Inspection Checklist #10 245

   PILLAR #11: WRITING STYLE—CONCISE AND SPECIFIC 250

      Inspection Checklist #11 255

   PILLAR #12: MOTIFS FOR COHESION AND DEPTH 260

Inspection Checklist #12 266

ADDITIONAL MIND MAPS YOU CAN CREATE 276

CONCLUSION 285

ABOUT THE AUTHOR...287

INTRODUCTION

There are many published books available that aim to teach writers how to write a novel, and while some focus on overall structure and others on the individual components that make up a novel (such as plot, characters, dialog, and setting), few, if any, take a holistic view of novel construction.

Why is a holistic view of novel construction essential? Because just as a building contractor cannot piece together the individual parts of a house without engineered blueprints for every facet of construction, a novelist cannot hope to build a novel without seeing the big picture and all that entails during every step along the way.

For every task required in building a house, a builder must know both his materials and his tools. You don't frame up a house with tar paper, and you don't use plastic pipe for gas lines. It takes time and effort to acquire the proper training to be proficient in any vocation. Novel writing is no exception.

Why Bother with Structure?

Instead of approaching a novel in a haphazard fashion, which often creates confusion and frustration, novelists can follow a simple set of blueprints that will help them construct novels that will stand up under the weight of scrutiny and the test of time.

A house that is built with strong, lasting, appropriate materials will hold up under adverse conditions. Novelists who learn not just which tools they need in their construction efforts but also how to wield those tools effectively, for the best results, will build solid stories that will last.

Is structure important? Absolutely. I critique and edit more than two hundred manuscripts a year, and most suffer from lack of workable structure. Some so much so that they really need to be round-filed. I cringe hearing how some of these writers have spent years penning their first novel (or perhaps even many subsequent ones), and often have spent additional years trying to get an agent to sign them. These are wasted years.

Does this mean there is only one way to construct a novel? Of course not. But there are time-tested, acceptable "rules" to novel construction, just as there are respected building codes designed to ensure a structure will not collapse, whether it is a house, a bridge, or a skyscraper. Regardless of what type of "structure" [read: genre] a novelist is attempting to build, it is prudent to work with blueprints that will ensure a sound one.

12 Key Pillars That Work Together

I've developed what I feel is a very approachable, easy-to-understand "set of blueprints" for novelists of any experience. This involves constructing twelve essential pillars, which are not simply individual novel components. Each of these pillars must work harmoniously (structurally) with all the others, and four hold the greatest weight of a story—those I call the four corner pillars.

Imagine your novel as a house. Or more like an ancient Greek building, such as the Parthenon. Made completely of marble, heavy marble—including the massive roof. Then imagine how strong those columns have to be to support such a gargantuan weight. If we liken the completed novel to the roof, then consider the pillars supporting the roof as the key to success. We want "fifty-ton" columns to support our roof so it will not only look sturdy but stand the test of time.

The four corner pillars have the toughest job providing the support for the entire structure. And so, as you use this workbook, you'll first be building those four corner pillars, and once they are sturdy and positioned just right, you'll move on to the other eight support pillars. These are the four corner pillars:

- **Concept with a Kicker**
- **Conflict with High Stakes**
- **Protagonist with a Goal**
- **Theme with a Heart**

The eight secondary pillars provide the additional support to your story, and are developed after the four corner pillars are built:

- **Plot and Subplots in a String of Scenes**
- **Secondary Characters with Their Own Needs**
- **Setting with a Purpose**
- **Tension Ramped to the Max**
- **Dialog—Compressed and Essential**
- **Voice—Unique for Each Character**
- **Writing Style—Concise and Specific**
- **Motifs for Cohesion and Depth**

But keep in mind: just as a house builder must see the big picture all the way through construction—from foundation to finish materials—novelists must keep their big picture continually at the forefront of their minds. This workbook is designed to help you tackle such a daunting, gargantuan task!

HOW TO USE THIS WORKBOOK

While you can use this workbook alone, you will get much more out of it, and understand this process more thoroughly, if you use it alongside *The 12 Key Pillars of Novel Construction*. The method in this workbook follows the book closely, which covers each of the twelve pillars in depth. Each time you get ready to work on a new pillar, read through the chapter in the book so you have a clear, deep understanding of the task ahead.

With each pillar you'll have questions to explore and answer, exercises to help you generate and strengthen your ideas, and examples of ways you can brainstorm and mind map your pillar. In addition, I join in the process with an idea of my own, to give you a step-by-step demonstration of how this process works alongside yours.

The last part of the book gives numerous additional examples of ways to mind map the twelve pillars, as well as how to combine them. You may want to work on larger pieces of paper for your mind maps, or use tag board. Don't let the constraints of the workbook limit your imaginative or curtail your exploration of your pillars.

In the *12 Key Pillars* book, twelve inspection checklists are provided for each pillar. These are questions you ask yourself about your novel and must be answered solidly to ensure you have a strong pillar. Builders are required to pass numerous inspections before the house they're building can ultimately get "signed off." If the inspector finds something wrong—not up to code, or in conflict with the blueprints—the builder has to fix it in order to pass that inspection. So, in keeping with this construction theme, I created these novel-building checklists to help writers examine their work for flaws or cracks that might cause collapse.

These checklists are expanded in this workbook, alongside many other prompts and exercises to help you nail each pillar (pun intended). While it's important to get those first four corner pillars of construction solid, because of this holistic approach to novel building, you'll want to move around through the workbook, strengthening pillars as needed, as you come up with new ideas, and as you brainstorm and mind map your connections between pillars.

If you find you need more space to generate more ideas, copy and print out extra work pages (it's a good idea to do this before you start to write on them). Keep all your pages in a folder or notebook, so when you begin to write or revise your novel, you can easily refer to these pages, which are your building blueprints.

Work on the Four Corner Pillars First

Take your time getting those first four corner pillars strong, and then move around the other eight pillars in whatever order suits you. Often writers will have plenty of great ideas about some of their novel components, but lack others. Each person's creative drive follows a different path, and that may even vary from novel to novel. You might start with a heavy theme you want to explore. Or maybe you envision a unique world in which to set your story. You may have an idea for a compelling protagonist. But these are individual pieces of the much-bigger picture.

You will bring in all these simmering ideas as random bits of materials, but once you use them in specific ways to construct each of the twelve pillars, you will see how those wild, disjointed, disparate-seeming components will come together in a clear and practical way.

Building a novel has its challenges, just as with building any complex structure. But writers don't have to guess how to piece a story together. All they need to do is build solid pillars using time-tested "building codes." Sure, it takes work, but it can be a whole lot of fun. Having blueprints eliminates a lot of unnecessary anguish, confusion, and (ultimately) failure.

So, grab your tool bag full of tools and jump right in. Work on these exercises and complete all your checklists so you can build that solid novel.

1

THE FOUR CORNER PILLARS

Your first steps in constructing a solid novel require building the four corner support pillars. You can work on these in any order, and you may find it best to move among them freely as you come up with ideas. The key to a strong, lasting, compelling novel is in those first four pillars, so take as much time as you need to work on these, and don't rush to move on to the rest of your novel elements until you have all four solid.

Think how a building would need those four pillars already formed and equal in size, shape, width, and weight when they are put into place. That's what you'll need to do before you can construct the remaining eight pillars, which work as additional supports for your novel.

For each pillar, you'll have some primary points to brainstorm, followed by your inspection checklist—which comprises twelve sets of questions to help you examine your structure. If you can answer all the questions to your satisfaction, you'll know you have that pillar in place.

So let's dive into the first pillar—Concept with a Kicker—which is often the most difficult one to get a handle on and is the weakest pillar in most novels. Be sure to **first read chapters 3 and 4 in *The 12 Key Pillars of Novel Construction*** first to get a good understanding of all the material.

PILLAR #1: CONCEPT WITH A KICKER

Writers are often confused about the difference between concept, idea, and premise. And no wonder. Writing craft books and instructors have differing definitions, many of which add to the confusion.

To make things simple, for the sake of clear, easy-to-grasp novel construction, let's break this down.

An idea is just a germ of a story. A lump of clay. Ideas are a dime a dozen, as they say. Not every idea has the makings of a great concept. This first corner pillar requires a concept with a kicker, which is much more than an idea.

Here are some examples of ideas:

- **A novel about the first manned mission to Mars**

- **A novel about man stuck on an island for two years alone**

- **A novel about a teenage girl who falls in love with a boy vampire**

- **A novel about a bunch of kids learning to be wizards at a wizard school**

- **A novel about an evil being who searches for his lost ring of power**

- **A coming-of-age novel about a boy who hitchhikes across the country**

As you can see from these "ideas," they are just a starting point for a deeper, richer concept. You may have lots of general ideas for a possible novel, but once you find an idea that intrigues you, you need to take it to the next step. You need to start molding that clay into shape.

Your Premise

Just what is a premise? A premise supposes something is going to happen. And that *something* requires a response.

You could say, for example: "I propose this (bad, scary, tense) situation, and this is what must be done to deal with it." As you might conclude, a lot of ideas fail even at this "premise" stage by not having a **compelling situation** that requires some **specific action**. This is where premise meets Protagonist with a Goal, Concept with High Stakes, and Theme with a Heart. Someone with some passion needs to deal with the situation in the midst of huge conflict.

Examples:

- "An evil power searches for a ring that's been lost for ages, and *in order to prevent him from taking over the world*, that ring must be destroyed."

- "A girl in Kansas gets taken over the rainbow to a magical land, and *somehow she must find her way back home*."

- "An alien race is coming back to destroy Earth, and so *young boys must be trained to become battle commanders to stop them*."

* In this workbook, I join in and take a random idea I thought up off the top of my head all the way through the same steps alongside yours, to show you ways you can use this process productively. It's important to test your idea to see if it has "novel" potential, and, if so, build twelve strong pillars to ensure success.

Let's start with your idea. See if you can **state your basic idea simply in one sentence.** Try a few variations:

Examples for my idea:

- *A man who's been struck by lightning eleven times risks his life to stop a killer.*

- *A terrorist is on the loose in the mountains, and a park ranger who has been repeatedly struck by lightning is the only one who can stop him.*

- *A man at war with lightning must fight it to stop a killer.*

Your examples:

_____

_____

_____

_____

_____

_____

_____

_____

Now, Ask "What If?"

One way to start fashioning your idea into a strong concept with a kicker is to ask "what if?" questions. This can help turn your cool idea into a premise. Every novel you've ever read and every movie you've watched can be fashioned into a "what if?" question. Why is this helpful? Because it takes the germ of an idea and starts moving it into the realm of concept.

Take a look at the "what if?" questions for the previous examples:

- "What if a simple, humble hobbit must take a ring of power to a dangerous land in order to destroy it and thus prevent the evil ruler from using it to take over the world?"
- "What if a girl who is taken over the rainbow has to get the broomstick of a wicked witch in order to return home to Kansas?"
- "What if a young boy, who is chosen to be the top battle commander, must train hard and risk lives to defeat an alien race from destroying Earth?"

Your "what if?" questions may be variations of the same basic idea, but they can help you explore the potential aspects of your idea.

"What if?" questions for my idea:

- *What if a man has to risk his life in a storm to save a hostage(s) from a serial killer?*
- *What if a cop who is afraid of lightning has to face down his greatest fear to save someone?*

- What if an antisocial park ranger who's been struck by lightning eleven times must reluctantly track down a killer to save lives?

Write some "what if?" questions for your idea:

What if . . .

_____

_____

What if . . .

_____

_____

What if . . .

_____

_____

What if . . .

_____

_____

Coming Up with a Kicker

A premise starts giving your idea purpose and shape. But that's not all it needs to become a concept with a kicker.

What is a kicker? A kicker is what turns your idea or premise into a terrific concept. A kicker is not a plot twist but an aspect to your story idea that makes a simple or ordinary situation intriguing. Just about any average idea (or one that's been done a thousand times) can be turned into a viable concept with a kicker. How?

Concept cannot be just about plot. A great concept for a novel can't hold up if it's just a good idea or an interesting premise. It has to have the support of the three other pillars. That's when the concept gets into high gear with a kicker. That's why a great concept sentence will not just include what the novel is generally about (plot) but will focus on the protagonist's goal, conflict with high stakes, and theme.

So, let's work on developing your kicker to turn that idea into something truly compelling. Bring to that tired old plot idea something unexpected, something intriguing—some factor or component that will shake the traditional, basic, simplistic story and make it a Concept with a Kicker.

First: Read through chapters 3–12 in *The 12 Key Pillars of Novel Construction* that cover the four corner pillars before you start the hard work on your Concept with a Kicker.

Here are three great ways to create a kicker:

- **Unusual Setting.** Come up with an unusual setting or locale for your novel that will make this story unique or fresh.

- **Unexpected Career or Hobby.** Choose an intriguing career or hobby for your protagonist that can turn your idea on its head.

- **Impacting World or Local Events.** By placing your story in a specific period in time and/or a place where some important event occurs, you can amplify your idea.

Think up some variations using these three factors, and see how you might generate a kicker for your story. If you think you have a good kicker, play around with ideas that can make your kicker even bigger, better, more impacting.

Let your imagination go wild, for here is the key place for your idea to bloom and grow.

1. Examples of unexpected settings:

- Boy meets girl . . . underwater (Mer-people? Scuba divers seeking sunken treasure?). Or while stuck in an elevator during a power-out. Or while serving together on a jury (or he's on the jury and she's on trial for murder).
- Man competes in a race . . . on the moon. Or through a jungle. Or across a city populated with zombies.
- Two men fight for the same woman . . . in a mental ward. Or while tunneling underground to get to freedom. Or in the White House.

As you come up with ideas, keep in mind your possible themes (your fourth corner pillar). If you want to explore themes of justice or racism, you might come up with *settings* that will create high tension and conflict (the third corner pillar), such as setting your story in a prison or in a place where racism abounds.

Key to your concept will be the goal you set for your protagonist. By coming up with a creative setting in which to place your character and show her going after her goal, you can make your story not only more intriguing, you can ramp up the stakes and the themes. This is all a part of holistic novel construction.

Setting might be part and parcel of your idea already, but play with it and see if you can come up with other possible locales or settings that will add a kicker to your idea.

A list of some unusual or unexpected settings for my idea:

- *The Rocky Mountains or other US Western mountains (where there are low incidences of lightning)*
- *Congested urban area where lightning usually can't strike (for some of the settings) but it does*
- *Mountains with lava tubes, subterranean cave systems, active volcano*
- *Mountains infested with ? Rabies, bees/wasps, other living threats? A "keep out" area due to contamination or ?*

List some unusual or unexpected settings that might work with your idea:

_____

_____

_____

_____

_____

_____

_____

2. Examples of unexpected careers or hobbies:

- Two people fall in love . . . an undertaker and an archaeologist. A cop and a professional jewel thief. A prison guard and a prisoner. A therapist and a serial killer.

- A woman who pursues a career of being a detective . . . in 10th century Japan. Or Victorian England.

- A computer nerd who gets messages from "the great beyond" and uses his skills to try to crack the "code" to the dead.

- A man who creates perfumes to lure and control women.

A list of some unusual or unexpected careers or hobbies for my idea:

- Park ranger (I know I want this to be his vocation)

- Expert in lightning since he's been struck repeatedly. Member of some lightning victims' club

- Science nerd or geologist—some specialty that ties in with love of wilderness—that will be key (motif?) in story

- Former cop (some park rangers are law enforcement officers), but got disabled on the job by lightning

- Has some uncanny sixth sense, paranormal ability, telekinesis (heightened electromagnetic field?) due to lightning strike? ** (I starred this idea!) so this topic is a huge hobby/interest for him (and source of grief)

List some unusual or unexpected careers or hobbies that might work with your idea. These may apply to your protagonist and/or secondary characters:

_____

_____

_____

_____

_____

_____

_____

_____

_____

_____

Don't choose a random setting or career or event just because it's unusual. Every choice you make for your novel has to have a specific purpose. Think about the heart of your story, what it's really about (which is theme), then come up with setting, career, and scenarios that will best serve the interests of your premise and concept.

Additional exercise: Think about some of your favorite novels. Make a list of each protagonist's career or hobby that is important to his character. Consider why and how this interest enhances the character and story.

3. Examples of unexpected world or local events (which can be invented):

- A love story set on an island after a war destroys most of the world. Or set in the crowds in Dallas when JFK was shot. Or set in a penthouse suite on a beach when a huge tsunami hit. Or set in a submarine during an alien invasion.

- A brilliant man races to find a cure for a killer disease . . . when an earthquake strikes and the power goes out. Or during the worst winter on record. Or while his mind is succumbing to Alzheimer 's disease.

- A girl tries to find her missing father . . . on the streets of New York as the Trade Towers fall. Or as a terrorist shuts off all the power in Anchorage, Alaska, in the dead of winter.

A list of some unexpected world or local events for my idea:

- *Huge killer lightning storm (of course!)*

- *Earthquake or other regional disaster—causes volcano to start erupting? Bomb goes off? Plane crash or lightning starts a wildfire?*

- *No world event applies or might affect protagonist and story, but some local event could hinder or complicate if it brings runners or hikers up into the mountains. Fourth of July celebration or?*

- *Terrorist attack/threat? Caused by the nemesis?*

- *State elections/local celebration that brings a lot of people to town—about an issue terrorist is passionate about and uses violence to make a statement*

List some unusual or unexpected world or local events that might work with your idea:

_____

_____

_____

_____

_____

_____

And these aren't the only ways you can tweak an idea to make it zing with concept. Characters' hobbies, passions, past hurts, secrets, or unusual upbringings—the possibilities are only limited by your imagination.

Other unexpected factors that might help me create a kicker:

- Protagonist has an obsession and personal relationship with lightning—which is his true nemesis in the story, not the serial killer/terrorist.

- The story is more about the protagonist and the issues of controlling his environment vs. giving in to the greater power of the elements to acquiesce to his destiny (theme of control—do we let go to have it?).

- Hero plagued with past guilt over his brother's death (feels it's his fault, has penance to pay—lightning strikes). He can't become whole until he purges that.

List some other unexpected factors that might create a kicker for your concept:

_____

_____

_____

_____

_____

_____

_____

_____

_____

Additional exercise: Do a search on Amazon.com or some other online bookseller for books in your genre. Read the description copy for a dozen of these novels and see if you can spot a concept that has a strong kicker. Does the description intrigue you at all? Or does the story sound like the same old, same old? If you notice an intriguing kicker, ask what intrigues you. Does the book present a twist on the usual setting, career, or time period? Does it take place during an interesting time in history? Think how you might twist the basic plot of each novel so that it has a kicker, if it doesn't seem to have one.

Brainstorm Key Questions

When you are brainstorming your ideas and homing in on the one you want to develop into your next novel or if you are already writing a novel but feel it's not all that extraordinary, spend some time thinking about the kicker.

Here are some of the questions you want to ask. These should get your creative juices stirring. Try to freewrite your ideas.

What is unique and compelling about my central idea for my novel?

My idea: It's not just a typical suspense thriller of a cop chasing after a killer. It's all about the lightning and this man obsessed with gaining control over lightning (symbolic on many levels, great motif!). His nemesis is this element, while he goes after a killer and rescues hostages.

Your idea:

_____

_____

_____

_____

_____

_____

How can I tweak this idea and infuse it with something outrageous, tense, full of conflict?

My idea: The lightning can almost be sentient, chasing him down. Maybe becomes paranormal (or to him? He may think he's going crazy). Maybe he knows the killer from his town, his past? Or knows one of the hostages? Maybe there are bigger stakes than just stopping a killer? His confrontation of lightning creates huge environmental dangers and effects.

Your idea:

_____

_____

_____

_____

_____

_____

Can I elevate the stakes dramatically for my main character to give the concept heightened drama and suspense?

My idea: In addition to the expected conflict and stakes of the basic cop/killer chase plot, the weather and other natural plaguing incidents can add to the tension. His life under attack while he's trying to do his job. Add in other characters that get in the way and have other agendas? Key: if he fails, he has to impact more than just himself—others and the environment? He has to risk his life and lives of others to reach his goal.

Your idea:

_____

_____

_____

_____

_____

_____

_____

What kind of goal can I give my main character that will seem impossible to reach?

My idea: Well, he wants to stay alive, which will start to seem impossible and make him want to quit. He also wants to save the hostages and stop/kill the killer. He has to face his nemesis (lightning), which he does not want to do, in order to reach his goal (willing to die, maybe does?) His visible goal of saving people has to include his need to control lightning, which would seem impossible but could be essential to my story.

Your idea:

_____

_____

_____

_____

_____

_____

What controversial or sensitive issues or themes can be at the core of this idea so that it will tug on readers' hearts?

My idea: Sacrifice and redemption, big themes! He has to come to a place where he is willing to die and give in to his nemesis (which maybe he learns really isn't his nemesis after all but his savior of sorts). Concept forms around these themes, as the climax has to be his giving his life to stop the killer and save those at risk.

Your idea:

_____

_____

_____

_____

_____

How can I twist the whole idea so that it poses an intriguing dilemma or conflict?

My idea: The intriguing conflict is his fight with lightning in the midst of chasing a killer. The conflict is more within himself than with the external forces. Or he can find ways to channel/harness the lightning so that he can use it to reach his visible goal.

Your idea:

_____

_____

_____

_____

_____

_____

These questions bring in the other three key corner pillars—Protagonist with a Goal, Conflict with High Stakes, and Theme with a Heart. I mentioned that in order to have that Concept with a Kicker, you need to develop it with the three other corner pillars, and so these questions are meant to get you start thinking holistically.

Remember, to have a strong, compelling novel, it has to be more than a great idea or a clever premise. It needs to have some interesting aspect to it that pushes it into the realm of high concept—which basically means that people will want to read your book just from hearing your one-sentence story concept (which you'll work on as you start answering the questions in your checklist).

24

Kickers Will Vary Based on Genre

You might argue that some novels really don't need a kicker. Maybe you write formulaic romantic suspense or cozy mysteries or traditional Westerns. Does that mean you don't need a kicker? You may not need much of one to sell books, but if you want to write a great story, one that will stand the test of time and be memorable, you'll want to infuse your basic plot with a kicker.

It doesn't have to be monumental, but it's not hard to take a good idea and make it a great one with a kicker. As we've gone over, sometimes all that is needed to turn an idea into a viable novel concept with "legs" is to create an intriguing framework in which to set your story.

Is a Kicker a "High Concept"?

You may have heard the term "high concept." Michael Hauge, Hollywood screenwriting consultant, gives this definition as it pertains to movies (however, this applies agreeably to novels as well): "A high concept is a story concept that is strong enough that it will draw an audience without any other components. It is not dependent on casting, name director, execution, word of mouth . . . it is simply the story idea alone that will promise an emotional experience."

Think about a novel like *The Hunger Games*. If all Suzanne Collins came up with was "a girl in an oppressive dystopic future society has to struggle to survive (and gets caught in a love triangle)," do you think she would have sold that book to a publisher? If the kicker—the games themselves—was not a part of the book(s), she might have had a good idea and maybe could have sold a few copies—but perhaps not millions.

The kicker in that novel was a fascinating predicament. Featuring a game that forced children to murder one another, Collins introduced an element into the primary structure (pillar) that could support the entire novel. Again, this is not just an idea or premise or plot point of a novel.

This is a foundational concept that creates tension, mystery, and curiosity. It makes readers ask questions they really want the answers for. How in the world could a child make it out alive? What kind of emotional damage would these children suffer?

Kickers make readers ask questions they want answered. Kickers move the ordinary into the extraordinary. Kickers take ordinary ideas and put them on steroids.

Can you think of some great novels or movies that have a terrific kicker? Have you ever had someone tell you a brief summary of a novel they'd just read or a movie they'd just seen and you knew instantly you would have to read or see it? Think about what intrigued you and why. Then see if you can generate that kind of a kicker for your story— something that will get listeners intrigued when you tell them. If people say to you, "Wow, what a great idea. I want to read that book!" you will know you have clinched your kicker.

A Caveat

I'll concede this point: not all novels have to have a high-concept kicker. If you are writing formula romance for Harlequin's Love Inspired series, you may not need anything that outstanding. Same with a post-modern literary work—although I would pose the challenge that with every novel, a writer should be able to come up with a kicker of some sort.

I'm all about writing great stories—ones that will stand the test of time, like a well-built house. Yes, well-built romance novels written to formula are structured well. And many will endure the ravages of time. Formula novels follow "building codes" and are a fine example of a builder using a blueprint correctly to build a specific kind of structure.

But if you are striking out "on your own" to create an original novel with a high concept, you'll need a great kicker.

Inspection Checklist #1

Concept with a Kicker

Here are the sets of questions and exercises on your inspection checklist, and more. Take time to think these through and answer them. If you haven't yet come up with the solid answers you need for some of these questions, leave them blank and come back to them later, after working on the other three corner pillars. But be sure to get them all answered to your satisfaction before you move on to the eight other essential pillars of novel construction.

Question Set #1:

What is your basic idea for a novel? Write this as a statement:

_____

_____

_____

_____

List three "What If?" questions that reflect your premise:

_____

_____

_____

_____

What is the kicker that twists an ordinary idea into something unique, original, and compelling? Try to explain in one clear sentence:

_____

_____

_____

_____

To have a strong Concept with a Kicker, you'll need to know how the other three corner pillars come into play in your story. Consider these examples (from Netflix):

- *Maleficent*: "Turning the classic fairy tale 'Sleeping Beauty' on its head, this fantasy drama retells the story from the point of view of evil godmother Maleficent. While defending her homeland from invaders, the young Maleficent is dealt a cruel blow by fate." The kicker is having the evil antagonist be the protagonist of the story.

- *The Giver*: "In a future society called The Community, pain, war, and disease have been eradicated, as have individuality and free will. When a teenager named Jonas learns the truth about the real world, he must decide whether to reveal all or remain quiet." Note the high stakes, the protagonist's goal. The "what if?" is tied in with what Jonas will do with the secrets he uncovers. Also clear are potential themes. The unusual setting "frames" the well-used basic plot in a new setting.

- *Non-Stop*: "On a commercial flight at 40,000 feet, federal air marshal Bill Marks starts receiving text messages from a threatening blackmailer who claims he's on the airplane too. Can Marks identify his camouflaged adversary before he begins killing passengers?" No need to comment on the unique setting for this cop-chasing-crook story, or the kind of high stakes involved.

- *The Fault in our Stars*: "Teenager Hazel, who has pushed people away since her cancer diagnosis, reluctantly joins a support group, where she bonds with a boy named Gus. Together, they face the challenge of building a relationship under the shadow of terminal illness." Here's a great scenario for a typical love story—a Concept with a Kicker that has potential for a lot of emotional high stakes and themes. Falling in love knowing you could lose the one you love—or you could die and cause your loved one pain? That's huge.

- *Snowpiercer*: "The Earth's remaining inhabitants are confined to a single train circling the globe as revolution brews among the class-divided cars." Again, a unique setting/situation to gives a twist to the commonplace plot of man against man.

Now, rewrite your one-sentence concept statement that includes your protagonist and his/her goal (you may choose to come back to this after working through the second pillar section):

_____

_____

Now, rewrite your one-sentence concept statement that notes the central conflict in your novel and what is at stake (you may choose to come back to this after working through the third pillar section):

_____

_____

Now, rewrite your one-sentence concept statement that includes your theme(s) (you may choose to come back to this after working through the fourth pillar section):

_____

_____

Now, try to write a 2-3 sentence pitch that includes all four corner pillar elements to create a cohesive, complete concept statement: (Think of how your novel, now a movie, would be listed and promoted.)

_____

_____

_____

_____

_____

Describe your idea, and explain how it's like a lot of other ideas out there:

_____

_____

_____

_____

_____

Now write a short blurb explaining how your kicker makes this common story unique:

_____

_____

_____

_____

_____

Question Set #2:

In what ways is your kicker tied into your protagonist's core need? (You may choose to come back to this after working through the second pillar section.)

_____

_____

_____

_____

_____

In what ways is your kicker tied into your protagonist's greatest fear?

_____

_____

_____

_____

_____

In what ways is your kicker tied into your protagonist's deepest desire?

_____

_____

_____

_____

_____

How does your protagonist's goal for the book embody or showcase your concept and kicker?

_____

_____

_____

_____

_____

Question Set #3:

What one element or focus makes you excited about your concept?

_____

_____

_____

_____

_____

Why will it also excite readers?

_____

_____

_____

_____

_____

List three ways you could make it into something controversial:

_____

_____

_____

_____

_____

_____

Question Set #4:

Picture a movie poster for your novel. What one key scene is pictured on it that embodies your concept and kicker? Describe it.

_____

_____

_____

_____

Now explain why you chose that scene:

_____

_____

_____

_____

Does it reveal something about your novel's themes? If so, what? If not, can you think of a way to infuse that key scene with some thematic import?

_____

_____

_____

Question Set #5:

What is the main gut response/emotional reaction you want your concept to evoke in your reader? Explain.

_____

_____

_____

_____

What are some ways you can tweak your concept so the reaction will be stronger?

_____

_____

_____

_____

_____

Ask: Why do you want your reader to react to your concept this way?

_____

_____

_____

What take-home thought or feeling do you hope to leave the reader with when he finishes reading your novel? How does your concept and kicker ensure this will come across?

_____

_____

_____

_____

Question Set #6:

What possibilities does the kicker add to your concept in the way of higher stakes and deeper conflict?

_____

_____

_____

_____

_____

_____

How might your kicker create higher stakes for the world at large (beyond your protagonist's life)?

_____

_____

_____

_____

_____

Question #7:

What themes, issues, or volatile topics does your kicker involve?

_____

_____

_____

_____

List some ways you can add them to the story line:

_____

_____

_____

_____

_____

Question Set #8:

What iconic scene can you write in your novel that will showcase the essence of your concept and kicker?

_____

_____

_____

_____

_____

_____

How can you make it even bigger, more intense?

_____

_____

_____

_____

Question #9:

State your concept with your kicker in one sentence. Include the central conflict and stakes:

_____

_____

_____

Can you tweak your kicker so the stakes are even higher? Try to show this below:

_____

_____

_____

_____

_____

_____

Question #10

What happens (or will happen) in the climax of the novel that will show why your concept and kicker are unique and compelling?

_____

_____

_____

_____

_____

_____

_____

_____

_____

Question #11

What key way will your protagonist change by the end of the novel that ties in specifically with your concept and kicker?

_____

_____

_____

_____

_____

_____

_____

_____

Question #12

Think about your novel's premise or basic plot idea. Ignoring the kicker you came up with, what three other, different kickers can you think of? Is one better than your initial idea? If so, consider using it instead.

_____

_____

_____

_____

_____

_____

**Write a one-paragraph summary of your novel highlighting your
Concept with a Kicker:**

_____

_____

_____

_____

_____

_____

_____

**Now write a one-paragraph summary of your novel highlighting your
Concept with a Kicker _but including your protagonist's goal, central
conflict, and theme_ (the other three corner pillars):**

_____

_____

_____

_____

_____

_____

_____

_____

_____

Mind Mapping Your Idea into a Concept with a Kicker

One of the best ways to generate ideas in a creative, uninhibited way is to mind map. **(Read chapters 27–29 in The 12 Key Pillars of Novel Construction to understand what mind maps are and how they are created.)** All the ideas you came up with on the prior pages can also be played with on a mind map, which can lead to other ideas as well as wander off into other pillar components.

You can create a small mind map on the pages provided here in the workbook, or get large pieces of tag board, or tape lots of pieces of paper together to create a big poster-sized work area. Use colored pens or pencils, and let your imagination loose. There are no rules when it comes to mind mapping, so have fun. Keep all your extra maps in a folder.

This part of the novel-creation process is where you really need to turn OFF your internal critic and editor. Give yourself permission to be as crazy as you want. You might surprise yourself with more than one great concept for a novel.

As I've done with the preliminary construction on the first pillar, I'm going to create and insert a mind map of my initial brainstorming for my new project idea. You do not have to mind map the way I do. Although, try to play with all the answers and ideas you came up with as you went through the various questions posed in this section on Concept with a Kicker.

You may want to do multiple mind maps as you generate more ideas. Just keep at it until your concept gels into the very best possible—one that brings into play the other three corner pillars. You'll note in my mind map I section off three corners to start exploring how those other pillars connect to this one.

Most of the pillars can benefit from mind mapping (I've left out the pillars on dialog, voice, and writing style). I hope my examples help you see how you can generate ideas and give you a holistic view of your novel.

My Mind Map to Generate a Concept with a Kicker

Protagonist + Goal

Hero's goal to stop killer tied in with spiritual goal and inner motivation to conquer lightning and face down his past to reach the visible goal.

Kicker

Not just a cop-chase-killer
- his relationship to lightning
- paranormal abilities/aspects
- personification of lightning?
- lightning as true nemesis
- must use his powers to face his fear + his enemies (spiritual + actual)

Concept

a man struck by lightning eleven times has to face his fears + guilt and stop a terrorist/free hostages

concept statement →

conflict/stakes

what's at stake?
- his life
- others with him
- bigger stakes -
    - city + environment at risk by his challenge of lightning + wielding his powers (telekinetic)
- people can (will?) die by his pursuit of his goal

Themes

Sacrifice - he has to be willing to lose his life to save it (and others)

redemption - through sacrifice + facing truth

courage to face truth and the past

mastery over fear

Being true to self is the only path to peace?

Your Mind Map to Generate a Concept with a Kicker

PILLAR #2: PROTAGONIST WITH A GOAL

If you want to write a compelling novel, then you need to be sure all the elements of your story work together for one main purpose.

What purpose? To follow your protagonist as he strives to reach a goal. Huh? Does that sound too pat to you? I imagine it does, to many writers—especially beginners.

You need both an empathetic and intriguing protagonist and a precise visible goal for him. It's not enough to showcase a "cool character" that you feel is unique. There has to be a reason you are writing an entire novel about him. And he needs something to care about, to want. All too often beginning writers feature protagonists that are boring, unappealing, or lacking ambition. These characters have no interests or passions, no real core needs, no purpose in life. No one wants to spend hours reading about such a character.

Establishing a meaningful, riveting goal for your protagonist is the key to a great novel—a goal that brings into play consequences and high stakes. So spend time working on your protagonist and goal, but keep in mind what stakes you might set up if he pursues that goal. The bigger, the better, when it comes to stakes.

I discussed in the prior sections the need to focus on the four essential corner pillars first before "building" the rest of your novel—Concept with a Kicker, Protagonist with a Goal, Theme with a Heart, and Conflict with High Stakes. Now that you've got Concept with a Kicker under your belt, we're going to delve into the important aspects of creating a compelling protagonist and how this goal of his or hers is the linchpin for the four supportive pillars.

First: Read through chapters 3–12 in *The 12 Key Pillars of Novel Construction* that cover the four corner pillars before you start the hard work on your Protagonist with a Goal.

Brainstorm Key Questions

Spend some time brainstorming these questions meant to get you thinking about your protagonist. Before digging into the checklist, you want to make sure you have a compelling, empathetic protagonist. These should get your creative juices stirring. Try to freewrite these ideas.

Who is Your Protagonist and Why?

Before you can dig into your protagonist's goal, you need to make some decisions about your protagonist. Don't focus on superficial things like appearance (hair and eye color, etc.). Those aren't important.

First, write a short paragraph about who your protagonist is:

My character: He's a survivor, compassionate, energetic (all things that can relate to lightning), driven, smart. He loves nature, so became a park ranger, but is at war with lightning (he's been struck many times and is now paranoid, obsessed, even manic secretly about this war). Has secret fear something is wrong with him, struggles with personal relationships (he lost someone he loved, his fault, he thinks). So often isolates, a loner, outspoken and frank with his opinions, doesn't tolerate weakness or lack of honor. Feels he must prove himself, be redeemed, believes he is either targeted/chosen for some greater good (but worries he has delusions of grandeur) or is being punished for his brother's death.

Your character:

_____

_____

_____

_____

_____

_____

_____

_____

_____

How to Create a Compelling Protagonist

Readers want to care about your protagonist, whether he is a heroic type or a dark/negative hero. And they want that to happen quickly, within the first few pages of being introduced to him. They want to be able to relate to your hero. So what can you do to ensure this will happen? Here are some things that make a character empathetic:

- **Put him in trouble.** Readers commiserate with characters facing problems, and especially ones they can relate to.

- **Give him some talent, skill, or admirable ability.** We like characters who excel at something.

- **Make him the victim of some unfortunate circumstance.** As with trouble, readers have compassion for a character who has had to suffer unjustly or due to some tragedy.

- **Make him funny.** We enjoy characters who have a sense of humor, and who might even be self-deprecating or don't take themselves too seriously.

- **Make him kind, noble, generous, gracious.** In other words, give some glimpse that he is a good person with a kind heart.

- **Show a glimpse of greatness.** This ties in with the item above. Whether your character is a heroic type, an ordinary Joe or Jane, or a dark brooding negative protagonist, showing some potential to be better, be great, or want to change is empathetic.

- **Make him passionate about something.** This is the key to your story as well. For, your protagonist has to pursue a goal, and if he really doesn't care all that much about reaching that goal, readers won't care either.

What makes your protagonist unique and compelling? What items on the above list apply to him or her?

My character: His problem with lightning and his inner fears, self-doubt make him compelling. He's in trouble (dangers all around). His skill is in his outdoor smarts, survival, special powers due to lightning strikes (very compelling). He also "sees" (lightning motif) through people's phoniness to their truth/true character/motivation. This is also a gift he got from the lightning. He can tell when people lie or when they are hiding things. Maybe even gets "flashes" of insights of truth about them. He's passionate about his goals and good at heart. Certainly is a victim of unfortunate circumstance with all those lightning strikes!

Your character:

_____

_____

_____

_____

_____

_____

_____

_____

The Core Need

Understanding your character's core need is crucial. Why? Because the core need creates the inner motivation for the character to pursue his outer goal. To get to your character's core need, answering these questions on your inspection checklist will help (you may want to skip ahead and work on those first before continuing in this section, if you're unclear about your protagonist's core need).

The inner motivation provides the emotional/spiritual goal for your story. It drives the outer plot that has your character going after that visible goal. These two goals are essential to forming a strong pillar.

Once you are clear about your protagonist's core need, you should be able to state your two goals for your protagonist.

What is your protagonist's core need? (What does he want more than anything right now and why?) What in his past or upbringing created this need?

My character: He wants to be free of this burden—to conquer lightning and stop living in fear. He has been running from this but now events make him face his fear head-on. He also needs to be free of guilt regarding the mistake he made that cost him to lose his brother. In other words, he needs to find a way to forgive himself (as he sees the lightning attacks as a kind of divine punishment). This core need pushes him hard and often makes him intolerant of others and a loner. But he knows he needs healing, peace, and to feel set free to live unburdened (and to be able to love).

Your character:

_____

_____

_____

_____

_____

_____

_____

_____

_____

_____

The Primary Goal Must Be Visible

Your protagonist must have a visible goal for the story, and usually that goal is "cemented" by the 25% mark of the novel. However, the inclination, formation, and core need set up at the start of the story should prepare for the goal. Usually some inciting incident occurs early on (within the first 10% of the novel) that starts the "hero" or "heroine" in a new direction. And ultimately, that direction will push the protagonist toward that riveting goal—which is at the heart of your concept with a kicker.

What do I mean by visible? Something substantial, not esoteric or emotional or spiritual.

Your goal for your main character can't be nebulous, like "she wants to find love in the end." She needs a very specific goal readers can picture. You should be able to describe your hero's goal to someone in a way that they can see it played out in their mind as if on the silver screen. Why is this important?

Because your novel is a specific story about specific characters needing and wanting something specific. There is no novel without characters. And if the characters don't have any goals, then what is the point to your story? Characters have to have deep core needs, desires, secret fears, impossible dreams. These are the factors that drive the story, like fuel for an engine.

Michael Hauge, story master, claims there are only five basic types of goals a protagonist can pursue, and that every strong story uses one of these:

- The need to win (competition, the love of another)
- The need to stop (someone, something bad from happening)
- The need to escape
- The need to deliver (a message, one's self, an item)
- The need to retrieve—(a magic ring, a hidden or lost treasure, a lost love)

This may seem so simplistic, it might be hard to believe. And maybe you think it doesn't even need to be discussed, since it's so obvious. But the protagonist's goal is often glaringly missing from many manuscripts written by aspiring authors.

Without that visible goal, your book could end up just a string of scenes—maybe some exciting scenes. But scenes without a point to them. Without that goal, your novel will be unfocused, wandering, and vague.

What basic story type does your novel showcase? Explain.

My story type: The need to stop this killer, but also to stop the lightning from controlling his life.

Your story type:

_____

_____

_____

How does that core need inform the visible goal for your story?

My character: His visible goal will be to stop the killer and any other dangers tied in with his human nemesis. However, this visible fight parallels the spiritual one, which is also a kind of visible goal as he battles the lightning and the physical manifestations of danger in nature (which he feels are personal attacks).

Your character:

_____

_____

_____

_____

_____

_____

Character Arcs

Writers are told characters have to grow and change, perhaps learn some important life lesson by the end of the novel. Or maybe not.

There are plenty of novels that don't show much of a character arc. Rather, the focus of the book is the plot. Genres like thrillers and action/adventure sometimes are all about plot, with the characters there to serve the plot, rather than the other way around. Some readers don't care about character growth or change. And that's fine. Readers read for many different reasons. Some novels are hilarious rides or tense suspense, and the protagonist doesn't "grow" or "learn anything" by the end of the novel. Part of that is genre; part is the author's choice.

But if that's the case, then the burden of the novel rests on the plot (and on the engaging writing style), and a writer tackling such a story will need to be sure to have that clear visible goal for the protagonist. And that goal should be tying in with the theme and featuring some very solid conflict (the third and fourth corner pillars) or that story might have some substantial fatal flaws.

You Still Have to Have a Goal

With or without a strong character arc, know that you still must have a protagonist with a clear goal. A thriller in which a character is being chased and is running for his life (such as *The Bourne Identity* and other thrillers) may seem to portray a protagonist without a goal. But, to the contrary, Jason Bourne and the like have very clear goals. The goal may be to get through/out/somewhere alive. And Jason Bourne not only needs to find a place of safety, he also needs to find out who he really is, which is the kicker to the basic chase-'em concept. Thrillers that appear to have no real protagonist goal often have a very strong and obvious one.

Creating an empathetic, unique protagonist with a goal is essential, but that one component won't hold up a novel. You need the other three corner pillars to provide the complete structural support for your story.

As you go through your inspection checklist, you'll be connecting your protagonist and goal to Concept with a Kicker, Conflict with High Stakes, and Theme with a Heart. If you can't answer some of the questions right now, leave them until after you work on the other three corner pillars. But don't move on to the eight secondary pillars until you have all four corner pillars strong.

> *Additional exercise:* Grab five of your favorite novels. Read the back cover copy, and think about the story's plot. Jot down on paper what you find compelling about each protagonist. Why do you love this character? What is his visible goal in the novel? What is his spiritual goal or core need (inner motivation) that pushes him to go after his visible goal? What can you learn from this exercise that helps you with your story?

Inspection Checklist #2

Protagonist with a Goal

Here are the sets of questions and exercises on your inspection checklist, and more. Take time to think these through and answer them. If you haven't yet come up with the solid answers you need for some of these questions, leave them blank and come back to them later, after working on the other three corner pillars. But be sure to get them all answered to your satisfaction before you move on to the eight other essential pillars of novel construction.

Question Set #1:

What is your protagonist's clear, visible goal for the book?

_____

_____

_____

How will you hint at that in the first ten pages of her appearing in your novel?

_____

_____

_____

_____

Question Set #2:

What does your main character want more than anything else? What is she willing to do to get it?

_____

_____

_____

_____

_____

What can make it more dangerous, more impossible to reach?

_____

_____

_____

_____

Why is this goal so important to her?

_____

_____

_____

_____

_____

Question Set #3:

What spiritual/emotional goal have you set up for your protagonist in the beginning of the book?

_____

_____

_____

_____

_____

How will she reach that goal by the end (or fail to)?

_____

_____

_____

_____

Question Set #4:

Why and how is the protagonist's goal crucial to the overall story?

_____

_____

_____

_____

_____

How does it tie in with your concept and kicker?

_____

_____

_____

_____

_____

Question Set #5:

How does the protagonist's goal reveal the theme(s) of the novel? Explain.

_____

_____

_____

_____

_____

What take-home message/emotional response do you want your readers to have after the goal is reached at the end?

_____

_____

_____

_____

_____

Question Set #6:

How will reaching this goal change your protagonist?

_____

_____

_____

_____

_____

How can you make the change much bigger and affect more characters?

_____

_____

_____

_____

_____

Pick two secondary characters that will be greatly affected by your protagonist striving after her goal. How will this be shown in your novel?

_____

_____

_____

_____

_____

Question Set #7:

What is the biggest obstacle preventing your protagonist from reaching her goal?

_____

_____

_____

_____

How can you make it much worse?

_____

_____

_____

_____

_____

_____

How can it push her into despair and hopelessness before the climax?

_____

_____

_____

_____

_____

Question Set #8:

In what ways is your protagonist unique and fascinating, and yet very much like anyone else?

_____

_____

_____

_____

_____

What great flaw does he have that will hinder his reaching his goal?

_____

_____

_____

_____

_____

How will he overcome or face this flaw by the end of the book, and what will he learn from this?

_____

_____

_____

_____

_____

Question Set #9:

What deep secret is your protagonist keeping?

_____

_____

_____

_____

_____

How will this secret interfere or sabotage him as he strives toward the goal?

_____

_____

_____

_____

_____

Question Set #10:

What are your protagonist's greatest strengths and weaknesses?

_____

_____

_____

_____

What will readers love and hate about her?

_____

_____

_____

_____

_____

Can you find a way for her weakness to become her strength? How?

_____

_____

_____

_____

_____

_____

_____

_____

Question Set #11:

How will you show something vulnerable, heroic, and/or intriguing about your protagonist in the first scene in which she appears?

_____

_____

_____

_____

_____

_____

_____

_____

What is her greatest gift or skill? Why would this make her admirable or empathetic?

_____

_____

_____

_____

Question Set #12:

What very important lesson does your character learn by the end of the book that changes her view of herself and the world and that ties in with your core concept?

_____

_____

_____

_____

What does your protagonist learn by the end of the book that ties in with your main theme?

_____

_____

_____

_____

_____

Write a one-paragraph summary of your novel highlighting your Protagonist with a Goal:

_____

_____

_____

_____

_____

Now write a one-paragraph summary of your novel highlighting your Protagonist with a Goal _but including your concept, central conflict, and theme_ **(the other three corner pillars):**

_____

_____

_____

_____

My Mind Map to Generate a Protagonist with a Goal

Protagonist

"John" (name him later)
Give symbolic name / ally
Calls him Spark?

core
needs:

vocation:

His lightning strikes
pushed him into science,
physics, ESP studies.
But love of wilderness moved
him to be a park ranger
(former cop?)
special skills - powers from
lightning - heightened ESP
telekinesis - but also "sees"
truth from lies (shines "light")

* to be free of
  his guilt / fear

* to face his
  nemesis once
  + for all

* redemption,
  forgiveness, peace

* to not be lonely
  anymore or feel
  like a freak

2 Goals

spiritual goals

- find peace, relieved of guilt
  over brother's death/blame
  heal
  allow himself to love

Pain/loss

lost brother in lightning storm.
His guilt for taking him out on
lake (when kids) father also
blames him - began his war
with lightning

Plot Goal

- stop the killer
- save hostages
- end the crisis

Lies he believes:

- can never be forgiven
- he's to blame for death
- he's cursed
- is being punished by
  God or universe for
  his mistake

Your Mind Map to Generate a Protagonist with a Goal

PILLAR #3: CONFLICT WITH HIGH STAKES

Conflict is story. Hands down, a novel without inner and outer conflict is going to fail. Strong, pervasive conflict is an essential pillar of novel construction. But not just any ol' conflict will do. It must be paired with high stakes.

Conflict and stakes need to go hand in hand. What point is there in showing characters arguing, for example, if there is nothing at stake? Conflict without purpose only takes up valuable real estate in your novel without accomplishing anything of importance. Throw that scene out. Or rewrite it so the conflict serves a purpose.

Conflict must have consequences. Conflict must be accompanied by high stakes.

Random conflict between characters or in the form of disastrous events won't build a strong pillar. Readers won't care about such conflict. They want to see how this conflict is intertwined with the protagonist's pursuit of her goal and how it ties in with the story's concept and themes.

Not all conflict has to be huge. Life is made up of varying degrees of conflict, both inner and outer. And so, too, our characters should experience conflict in various ways and intensities.

However, amid all the various conflicts your characters will face between the beginning and end of your novel, there should be some central conflict that poses the main opposition or obstacle for your protagonist.

First: Read through chapters 3–12 in *The 12 Key Pillars of Novel Construction* that cover the four corner pillars before you start the hard work on Conflict with High Stakes.

It's been said that there are only four basic plot types, all of which focus on the central conflict in a story:

1. **Man against man**

2. **Man against nature**

3. **Man against society**

4. **Man against self**

You might have some variation of one of the above, such as with a character facing opposition from an alien race or a sentient machine. In most novels, though, conflict and opposition to something or someone is at the core of the story and works as a strong corner pillar of construction.

Which plot type applies to your novel, and how specifically is that central conflict expressed:

My idea: The central opposition is the lightning, so it's man against nature. Going after the killer (man against man) is also applicable but not the main source of conflict in the story. And with all his inner struggling, there is strong "man against self."

Your idea:

_____

_____

_____

_____

Conflict Is All about Your Protagonist's Goal

Conflict must be tailored such that it poses the highest stakes possible in regard to your protagonist attempting to reach his goal for the book. And tied in with this is the underlying theme of your story.

In your second checklist you were asked some questions about your protagonist and her goal. How can you make things worse for her as she tries to reach her goal? What or who can oppose her that could force her to risk everything she wants and loves? If you tailor your conflict to create the highest stakes possible for your protagonist, you are on the right track to constructing a strong corner pillar in your novel.

Public and Private Stakes

Stakes come in two forms—"public stakes" and "personal stakes" Public stakes affect the world at large. They are stakes that affect others besides your character. That might mean global stakes or small-town stakes.

The strongest stories are the ones that have both public and personal stakes in spades. And usually stories in which the *personal* stakes are the highest are the better stories.

Stakes are what is at risk for your character, for either gain or loss. Characters make choices and initiate action as they go after their goal, and every choice and action should have something at stake—something to gain or lose. Any story, however small scale and personal, can present huge stakes and huge consequences. How can that be? Because it's all about the character and her goal.

If you create a compelling story with a highly sympathetic protagonist who has a goal that means everything to her, then those stakes, for her, are going to be high. If her happiness lies solely in reaching that goal, then anything that prevents her from her heart's desire is going to be . . . well, heartbreaking—and not just for her but for the reader as well.

Here are some examples of movies that feature high stakes for characters, which, outside of the specific premise, might not be high:

- *Fly Away Home*: A girl is intent on saving a flock of geese by relocating them hundreds of miles away.

- *The Milagro Beanfield War*: A poor man with a tiny bean field goes up against a big development corporation for the right to water his plants.

- *Field of Dreams*: A man risks losing his farm because he believes he must build a baseball diamond on his property.

- **Billy Elliott**: An eleven-year-old boy trades boxing school for ballet lessons, to his father's ire, in hopes of one day getting into the Royal Ballet School.

- *Queen to Play*: A maid at a hotel decides to learn and master the game of chess, and it changes her life.

Each of these movies showcases protagonists who are deeply passionate about their goal. And as you learned from going over the first two corner pillars, any goal could be turned into a compelling one if the protagonist is passionate about it. When you add to the mix high stakes, risks, and adverse consequences for attempting to achieve that goal, you have the building materials for a strong novel.

In addition, each of these movies brings out strong themes. If you haven't seen some of the above films, watch them and jot down what themes are brought to the forefront of the story by means of the protagonist going after his or her goal.

Risk Must Match Passion

Always keep this in mind: the passion a character has must be equal to the "penalty" he will pay if he doesn't take the risk, and it's commensurate to the value the character places on the thing at risk. If something is precious to your character, he will be willing to risk much to get, save, protect, or retrieve it (visible goal). The more value this object or objective has, the more you can push the stakes higher. And the higher, the better. That way, any conflict introduced that threatens will be big.

If I asked you to jump into a raging river to save my ballpoint pen, would you do it? Would you be willing to risk your life for that? What about jumping in to save my child? You might love me or my child enough to risk your life to save her. Or your personal beliefs about honor and self-sacrifice may move you to jump in even if you hated me or had no fondness for children. It's all about motivation, character, and passion.

Big threats, high stakes, great risks—all make for solid novel structure. So build your corner pillar of Conflict with High Stakes with deliberation and careful attention. It will provide excellent support for your novel.

Additional exercise: Consider watching some of the above mentioned movies and/or your favorite ones and write a paragraph about each of the four corner pillars built into the story. Or choose a few of your favorite novels and do the same analysis. No doubt you will find all four pillars strong and interconnected and providing a solid framework for the story.

Brainstorm Key Questions

Spend some time brainstorming these questions meant to get you thinking about the central conflict in your story and what's at stake. Before digging into the checklist questions, it's good to get clear what is at stake for your hero and what is opposing her and why. These should get your creative juices stirring. Try to freewrite your ideas.

What is the central conflict in my novel? What makes it unique and/or compelling?

My answer: Having the protagonist fighting lightning is unique, for it seems crazy and impossible. Nature is at war with him, trying to stop him from reaching his goal of stopping the killer and saving his hostage(s). The killer creates conflict, yes, but he's not the true nemesis.

Your answer:

_____

_____

_____

_____

_____

_____

In one sentence, state what your protagonist is willing to risk and why:

My answer: He is willing to risk his life to stop the killer and face down his fears because it's the right thing to do and feels it will save his soul.

Your answer:

_____

_____

_____

_____

Now give a longer, deeper explanation for your character's inner and outer motivation—for why he is willing to risk so much to reach his goal:

My answer: He knows if he fails (again), he could not live with himself. He is at the end of his rope emotionally, spiritually, even physically as he fights lightning to do what's needed (the right thing) because he is honorable, determined, and passionate. He cannot tolerate violence and cruelty and so cannot let the killer win. And because he needs to conquer his fears and find a way to freedom (spiritually and actually?), he will do anything, even die.

Your answer:

_____

_____

_____

_____

_____

_____

_____

_____

Now explain why readers will think this is believable:

My answer: They will see his pain and fears and understand his motivation. They will see how much honor and compassion mean to him, and that he has suffered so much and doesn't want to keep on going this way. He doesn't feel his life is so valuable that it is worth saving if it means saving someone else because of his guilt over a past mistake and need to pay penance. It's believable to think he would be obsessed with conquering lightning after he's been struck so many times and feels cursed.

Your answer:

_____

_____

_____

_____

_____

_____

_____

In what way will you set up what is at stake or risk for your protagonist in the opening scenes?

My answer: The setup for the main plot with the killer/threat can be shown with the protagonist in town about to go to the mountains to work as he hears about the killer's actions and escape. This establishes the public dangers/stakes as well. With a storm brewing, we see his relationship to lightning and his core need to conquer his fear—showing the pain this is causing him, buried deep, and the guilt he has over his past. By setting up this core need, fear, and guilt, it sets up the danger of lightning for him. He senses this storm is after him (his powers are heightened), and fears this is to be his big battle, win or lose, against the lightning that has destroyed his life and happiness.

Your answer:

_____

_____

_____

_____

_____

_____

_____

What stakes do other characters face? Think about your primary ally and nemesis characters. What are they willing to risk and why?

My answer: The hostages face injury or death. My protagonist might have an ally, another lightning victim from his meetings, who cares about him and is willing to help him fight his fears (or makes him more afraid). The nemesis/killer is crazy and determined, so he will be willing to do just about anything to reach his goal. To add more to the cast, the hero can be enlisted by police/Feds on this case to track and catch, so they are all at risk from both killer and the wild elements and lightning. They risk their lives because it's their job.

Your answer:

_____

_____

_____

_____

_____

_____

_____

_____

Additional thoughts on the stakes you might bring into your novel?

_____

_____

_____

_____

_____

_____

_____

_____

Inspection Checklist #3

Conflict with High Stakes

Here are the sets of questions and exercises on your inspection checklist, and more. Take time to think these through and answer them. If you haven't yet come up with the solid answers you need for some of these questions, leave them blank and come back to them later, after working on the other three corner pillars. But be sure to get them all answered to your satisfaction before you move on to the eight other essential pillars of novel construction.

Question Set #1:

What is the central (outwardly visible) conflict in your novel?

_____

_____

_____

_____

How is this conflict similar to a lot of other novels and movies?

_____

_____

_____

_____

_____

How is it different or unique?

_____

_____

_____

_____

How will you introduce the central conflict early in the story? In what way?

_____

_____

_____

_____

_____

Question Set #2:

How does this conflict element pose problems for your protagonist?

_____

_____

_____

_____

_____

Now, can you make it much bigger, much worse? List some possibilities and their outcomes:

_____

_____

_____

_____

_____

_____

_____

_____

_____

_____

_____

Question Set #3:

What are the _personal stakes_ at risk due to this conflict in your story?

_____

_____

_____

_____

Explain why your protagonist is willing to risk these things for her goal. Why is she so passionate about her goal?

_____

_____

_____

_____

_____

How would she feel and what would she do if she couldn't reach her goal?

_____

_____

_____

_____

_____

Can you raise the stakes more for your protagonist? How? In what ways?

_____

_____

_____

_____

_____

_____

Question Set #4:

What are the things your protagonist loves and cherishes the most?

_____

_____

_____

_____

_____

_____

Can you set up the conflict so that he stands to lose those as he goes after his goal? Explain how:

_____

_____

_____

_____

Pick one precious thing or person your protagonist can lose near the climax of the story because of the conflict and high stakes. Can you think up a scene or moment to show this?

_____

_____

_____

_____

Question Set #5:

What public stakes are threatened by this central conflict component?

_____

_____

_____

_____

Who and what else will be adversely affected if your protagonist fails to reach his goal?

_____

_____

_____

_____

_____

_____

Can you make it worse? How?

_____

_____

_____

_____

_____

What allies can turn into foes by her choices and actions?

_____

_____

_____

_____

_____

What core beliefs of hers can be challenged?

_____

_____

_____

_____

_____

How can you complicate things so that it (seemingly) becomes impossible for her to reach her goal?

_____

_____

_____

_____

_____

Question Set #6:

What will happen right before the climax of the novel to show the conflict at its peak?

_____

_____

_____

_____

How will this push the hero into a dark night of the soul?

_____

_____

_____

_____

Question Set #7:

How can you make the conflict elements more personal so that it's more painful for your protagonist?

_____

_____

_____

_____

Who can betray her? Fail her?

_____

_____

_____

_____

_____

Question Set #8:

In what way is your central conflict embodying your theme?

_____

_____

_____

How does the conflict force your protagonist to make thematic choices in the novel, with the hardest choice at the climax?

_____

_____

_____

_____

_____

_____

Question #9:

How will the outer conflict component be resolved or eliminated (or left a threat) at the end of the novel so that the ending is satisfying and believable to readers?

_____

_____

_____

_____

_____

_____

Question Set #10:

What strong inner conflict is your protagonist dealing with? Explain where it came from, why it's there:

_____

_____

_____

_____

_____

_____

How and in what way will that inner conflict be resolved or eliminated by the end of the novel?

_____

_____

_____

_____

_____

Come up with two things she must choose between, both unthinkable:

_____

_____

_____

_____

_____

How does this showcase your novel's theme?

_____

_____

_____

_____

_____

Question #11:

Can you come up with at least five minor, different conflict components you can add to your plot that exacerbate the central conflict of your novel? List and explore them here:

_____

_____

_____

_____

_____

_____

_____

_____

_____

Question Set #12:

How does your protagonist change by the end of the book due to the central conflict?

_____

_____

_____

_____

How do her attitude and actions toward that conflict change, and as a result, how does the conflict itself change?

_____

_____

_____

_____

_____

What are the consequences your protagonist has to face at the end of the story due to his willingness to risk (positive or negative)?

_____

_____

_____

_____

Now write a short blurb explaining how your central conflict makes this common story unique:

_____

_____

_____

_____

_____

Write a one-paragraph summary of your novel highlighting your
Conflict with High Stakes:

_____

_____

_____

_____

_____

_____

_____

Now write a one-paragraph summary of your novel highlighting your
Conflict with High Stakes *but including your concept, protagonist's
goal, and theme* (the other three corner pillars):

_____

_____

_____

_____

_____

_____

_____

_____

My Mind Map to Generate Conflict with High Stakes

Other
outer conflicts

People

father— blames him
for son's death

girlfriend – wants from
him what he can't give

coworker – jerk with
his own agenda - guy
who wants only to
retire + save his own
skin

an ally – who wants to
help but causes conflict
by forcing John to face
his fears

Inner conflict
- feels cursed
- blames self
- shame, guilt
- afraid of his
  own powers
- feels cursed
  – inner conflict
  always driving
  him /paralyzing

outer
conflict

— lightning!
— other natural elements
stirred by conflict
(nature in mts.)
   landslides,
   earthquakes,
   forest fire

— ticking clock -
. hostages taken–
. storm worsening-
. killer's threat to
  hurt or kill if
  demands aren't
  met
(a bomb will
go off?)

Conflict with
high stakes

His passion
what does he care about most?
Truth, sanctity of life, justice

Personal Stakes
— his sanity
— his life
— his will to live
— his control

Public Stakes
If he knows his failure will result
in more death + destruction, more
pressure. Bigger consequences —
make his choices harder.
   May have to choose between doing
what is right and jeopardizing lives
of others (to stop killer)

Your Mind Map to Generate Conflict with High Stakes

PILLAR #4: THEME WITH A HEART

So far, we've looked at three of the four corner pillars that are the essential supports for your story, and you've been given your "inspection checklists" so that you can test your pillars to see how well they hold up your story. Those first three are Concept with a Kicker, Protagonist with a Goal, and Conflict with High Stakes. We're now going to explore corner pillar #4: Theme with a Heart.

In case you are wondering why plot isn't the fourth essential corner pillar, consider this: tension in a story has little to do with plot. Plot is all about what happens. Plot is "this happens first, then this happens next." And on and on until you get to the end of the book. But without concept behind and driving the plot, all you have is a string of possibly interesting scenes.

Theme is more important than plot in terms of supporting the whole of your story, and that's why it's the fourth corner pillar of novel construction. I called plot a vehicle for your theme. It's also the vehicle to showcase your concept, protagonist's goal, and central conflict. In other words, try to think of plot as functioning differently than the other elements in your story.

You may have one primary theme in your novel. Or you may have a number of themes running through it. Theme is the protagonist's inner motivation made universal, so as you work on your thematic ideas, keep in mind that what your protagonist wants more than anything should be something all readers can relate to, and by exploring that, you'll find your themes for your story.

First: Read through chapters 3–12 in *The 12 Key Pillars of Novel Construction* that cover the four corner pillars before you start the hard work on Theme with a Heart.

Ask Questions to Get to Your Themes

Does every novel have a theme—or need one? You might say no. But stop and think for a moment about your novel or any great novel you've read. Underneath all the plot layers of various sizes and colors and tastes lies something fundamental. Something at the heart of a story.

Ask yourself, "What's my novel about?" Then ask yourself: "What is my novel really about?" without talking about the plot. It may take some digging, but you will arrive at an answer that speaks to theme.

Theme is a glue that holds all the novel components together: characters, setting, conflict, plot, and, well, just about everything else. It sticks it all together.

Themes turn good novels into great ones. Themes take the story you have and make it better, deeper, more meaningful, more resonating, more universal. In other words, theme brings all your novel's elements together in purpose and presents life in a realistic, complex way. Novels with universal themes are the ones that stand strong and support a story.

By exploring why you are so jazzed about telling a certain story, you can mine rich themes and develop them.

Brainstorm Key Questions

When you are brainstorming your theme and homing in on the one you want to flesh out in your next novel or if you are already writing a novel but feel you haven't made this a deep enough story, spend some time thinking about your themes.

Here are some of the questions you might ask yourself. These should get your creative juices stirring. Try to freewrite these ideas.

Ask yourself: Why am I writing this novel? What excites me about the idea?

My answer: I'm fascinated by true stories of people who repeatedly get struck with lightning. I love the idea of a spiritual connection between man and nature, and one that makes the character explore his deepest fears, lies, and needs. I love the idea of self-sacrifice, and how by giving up our lives, we gain them. I want to set a novel in the wilderness because I love those stories of man pitted against the elements. I also love the concept of lightning personified (in my protagonist's mind) and in a way symbolizing his subconscious and conscience. I'm intrigued by electricity and the potential to explore it in paranormal and symbolic ways.

Your answer:

_____

_____

_____

_____

_____

_____

_____

Ask yourself: What excites me about the conflict in my story, and why do all these things *matter to me*?

My answer: Inner conflict that forces us to face our greatest fears and insecurities is important and fascinating to me. I love stories about characters who struggle within and try to become whole, which matters to me. I like the outer conflict with nature and an evil man because it provides opportunity for my protagonist to step up and make hard, personal choices, and understand what he is willing to die for and why. These, to me, are great issues that are universal.

Your answer:

_____

_____

_____

_____

_____

_____

_____

_____

_____

Ask yourself: What are the deeper elements below the surface of my story that I care about?

My answer: At the heart of my story is a man dealing with his place in the world and his self-worth. We often blame ourselves for something we did, carry guilt all our lives. We need healing and don't know how to get it. So we shut down and shut people out. So healing comes with facing fear down and being brave enough to look in the mirror, but also to find salvation and worth in sacrifice and truth.

Your answer:

_____

_____

_____

_____

_____

Themes are not just topics or subjects. The basic idea for your book is not the book's theme. You might say your book is about abortion or capital punishment. That is just the topic (idea). Ask: What are you saying about that topic through your characters? Whether you are taking a strong stance or none at all (just want to explore the topic), in order to have a plot, with characters who care about something, you will have theme.

State briefly what topic(s) your novel covers:

My answer: Basically good vs. evil. My book's topics include stopping evil/standing up and doing what is right as well as people who get struck with lightning or who have uncanny, extrasensory powers.

Your answer:

_____

_____

_____

_____

_____

What are you saying about this topic through your characters in the book? List some of the viewpoints expressed or embodied by them:

My answer: That you have to stand up to stop evil regardless of the risk or stakes (protagonist). That you have to face your greatest pain, fears, guilt (could be protagonist and ally). That you cannot control the forces that affect you but you have to learn to work with them, you shouldn't look at nature/forces as an enemy but maybe as an opportunity (?).

Your answer:

_____

_____

_____

_____

_____

_____

Does your protagonist stand up for something he believes in? What and in what way does he express this?

My answer: He stands up for being truthful and honest but has a hard time facing his own truths. He acts and doesn't just talk to stop evil and to face his fears. He uses his gifts and talents to help others.

Your answer:

_____

_____

_____

_____

_____

_____

Think about that dictionary definition of theme—"a specific concern." The operative word is *concern*. Someone, somewhere in your novel, is concerned about something—something bigger than just what to eat for breakfast or what clothes to wear. It's the job of your characters to embody or showcase your themes, and as we learned in the chapters about your protagonist, everything in a novel swings back around to the protagonist's goal. This is what's at the heart of your story and the heart of your theme.

Ask yourself: What is unique and compelling about my overarching theme for my novel?

My answer: My protagonist above all believes in the sanctity of life, revering nature and freedom. He believes in the higher good and a purpose to life beyond living for self. The theme of self-sacrifice will lay over the story and relationships. His goal to stop the killer as well as giving up his wish to control the elements and his "powers" falls under this theme.

Your answer:

_____

_____

_____

_____

_____

Ask: What is the "take-home" message or feeling I want to leave readers with when they finish my novel? How does this speak to theme?

My answer: That there is greater meaning and ultimate joy in sacrifice (on many levels). That you gain everything when you lose your self.

Your answer:

_____

_____

_____

_____

_____

_____

_____

If you could pick just one emotion or attitude that would hint at what your novel deals with, what would it be? (such as hate, forgiveness, grace, mercy, revenge . . .)

My answer: Aside from self-sacrifice, surrender.

Your answer: _____

If you could pick an emotional feeling that would define your protagonist at the start of the novel, what would it be?

My answer: a sense of being cursed, punished, guilt.

Your answer: _____

What about at the end of the novel? What does your protagonist feel after he's reached (or failed to reach) his goal?

My answer: Joy, fulfillment, enlightenment, understanding, strengthened by truth. Like Abraham, he passed the test of offering a life to prove willingness. He feels alive, strong, free by giving up his control.

Your answer:

_____

_____

_____

_____

_____

If your protagonist could tell you in brief summary what he learned from all he went through, what would he tell you?

My answer: I am forgiven, and must forgive myself, and be willing to lose myself. That is the path to joy and healing.

Your answer:

_____

_____

_____

_____

Does that give you something thematic to work with? What?

My answer: Sacrifice is a big theme and universal. It asks why someone would be willing to give up self for others. Deeper issues of self-worth and what gives you that belief in yourself is another theme. You need to face your fear and not run from it (outer conflict and inner). Can't let mistakes of the past destroy your life. Do the right thing even if others oppose/be true to yourself. The truth will set you free/what true freedom is and what its cost is.

Your answer:

_____

_____

_____

_____

_____

_____

_____

_____

_____

_____

Theme is said to be "the protagonist's visible goal made universal." What is your character's visible goal in your story?

My answer: To catch and stop or kill the killer so he can no longer be a threat.

Your answer:

_____

_____

Now, tell how that goal can resonate universally with any person at maybe any time in history, and try to state this in terms of theme:

My answer: It's the universal belief that evil must be stopped and not ignored. That one must act and not just talk when it comes to conquering evil. Good triumphs over evil. Regardless of cost, one must do the right thing. That there is some higher reward/purpose/fulfillment in sacrifice, which is a universal messianic theme.

Your answer:

_____

_____

_____

_____

_____

_____

_____

_____

_____

_____

_____

_____

Pitfalls of Working Themes into Your Story

Watch out for pitfalls when trying to develop themes in a story. Writers sometimes try to cram theme in their stories by preaching, lecturing, and long explanations—either via the characters or as author intrusion. You'll notice in the best movies and novels that have strong themes that those discussions centering directly on theme will feel organic to what is happening in the plot and to the characters.

Theme should manifest as a result of the events unfolding in your story that force characters to stand up, oppose, complain, dare, risk, turn away, stop, prevent, speak out, shut up—you get the point. Readers get the theme by watching you show (not tell) the story.

Although it's possible theme may naturally or accidently come through as a writer creates scenes and plays out her story, writing a novel with the intention of establishing, developing, and capitalizing on theme will make for a much better, focused novel.

Plot shows the story; theme *is* the story. Plot is the vehicle for theme. This is a good mantra to repeat as you plot out your novel.

Additional exercise: As you read the novels you love, jot down the themes you see presented. Then pay attention to how the writer brings them out. Use a yellow highlighter and mark up every line that speaks to theme. Then write down what ideas you get for your own novel's themes.

Inspection Checklist #4

Theme with a Heart

Here are the sets of questions and exercises on your inspection checklist, and more. Take time to think these through and answer them. If you haven't yet come up with the solid answers you need for some of these questions, leave them blank and come back to them later, after working on the other three corner pillars. But be sure to get them all answered to your satisfaction before you move on to the eight other essential pillars of novel construction.

Question Set #1:

Ask yourself, "What is my novel about?" Phrase it in terms of plot:

_____

_____

_____

_____

Now ask, "What is my novel _really_ about?" Answer it here, centering on the theme, not the plot:

_____

_____

_____

_____

Question Set #2:

List (or create) ten places (scenes, situations) in which your theme is explored in your novel—by whom, how, and in what circumstances:

_____

_____

_____

_____

_____

_____

_____

_____

_____

_____

_____

_____

_____

_____

_____

_____

_____

_____

_____

_____

How can you bring the theme out stronger in some of these?

_____

_____

_____

_____

_____

_____

_____

Question Set #3:

What iconic scene in your novel showcases (or will showcase) the heart of your theme? Describe why it's important to your story:

_____

_____

_____

_____

_____

_____

_____

_____

How can you blow it up as big as you can so it's the key scene?

_____

_____

_____

_____

_____

Question Set #4:

What are your protagonist's passionate views on this theme?

_____

_____

_____

_____

_____

How do these views tie in with her core need and goal for the story?

_____

_____

_____

_____

_____

Question Set #5:

Who challenges the views, actions, and beliefs of your protagonist in a way that involves your thematic elements?

_____

_____

_____

_____

_____

_____

In what ways can you make their opinions even stronger with higher stakes and greater conflict? Brainstorm some ideas:

_____

_____

_____

_____

_____

_____

_____

_____

_____

_____

_____

Question Set #6:

How is your theme showcased in the climactic scenes of your book?

_____

_____

_____

_____

_____

_____

Can you make the stakes higher and the choices harder for your protagonist? How?

_____

_____

_____

_____

Question Set #7:

If you can't identify any themes, can you come up with three key decisions your protagonist makes in your novel?

_____

_____

_____

Now, think of thematic topics to tie in with those decisions. Think of making inner motivation universal to all people. Ideas?

_____

_____

_____

_____

_____

_____

_____

_____

Can you now make those three key decisions more impacting? How, and for whom?

_____

_____

_____

_____

_____

_____

_____

_____

Question Set #8:

What wounds/past hurts have formed your characters? Start with your protagonist, and then list at least three important secondary characters:

_____

_____

_____

_____

_____

_____

_____

_____

_____

Can you find ways to tweak them to link thematically together?

_____

_____

_____

_____

_____

_____

_____

_____

Question Set #9:

Is your theme strongly emphasized in your final chapter? Yes? How might you bring it out even more?

_____

_____

_____

_____

_____

_____

No? Brainstorm three or more ways you might bring your key theme into the final scenes of your novel:

_____

_____

_____

_____

_____

_____

_____

_____

_____

_____

Question Set #10:

Find (or think of) five key scenes that showcase your theme. Briefly
summarize them here:

_____

_____

_____

_____

_____

_____

_____

_____

_____

_____

Now, think of a way to emphasize your theme in each of those scenes.
How can you bring theme to the forefront in each?

_____

_____

_____

_____

_____

_____

_____

_____

_____

_____

_____

_____

_____

Question Set #11:

Go back to your opening scene and ask: Does this scene introduce the key themes of my story? How? If not, list how you might accomplish this:

_____

_____

_____

_____

Is this really the best scene to open with that will introduce your themes? If not, play with some ideas that might:

_____

_____

_____

_____

_____

_____

_____

Question #12:

Can you come up with a line your protagonist can repeat (out loud and/or in his head) at least three times in the novel (best if that includes the first and last scenes) that will voice his feelings about the theme? What is it?

_____

_____

_____

_____

_____

_____

Write a one-paragraph summary of your novel highlighting your
Theme with a Heart:

_____

_____

_____

_____

_____

_____

_____

Now write a one-paragraph summary of your novel highlighting your
Theme with a Heart *but including your concept, protagonist's goal,
and conflict with high stakes* (the other three corner pillars):

_____

_____

_____

_____

_____

_____

_____

_____

_____

My Mind Map to Generate Theme with a Heart

Theme + Protagonist

- Sacrifice - must give his life to save others
- Redemption - only through putting others first
- Stop evil - standing up for for is right / speaking up
- must face one's feas/ Past / guilt

What's at the heart of my story?

- a man struggling with guilt over past mistakes
- he can't forgive himself
- feels he's being punished by God - punishment shown through the lightning man vs. nature
- sees his strange powers as curse instead of a gift.

Theme

Theme with High Stakes

Expressed through characters:

- killer goes after his goal but loses in the end (good wins)
- father blames hero, won't forgive, so is always in pain (must forgive to heal)
- coworker who sabotages/doesn't stand up against evil— selfish Shows no peace from selfish course

concept + Theme

core of concept is the theme of sacrifice. Also the need to face the truth.

Light of truth is painful (like being struck with lightning) but necessary to heal.

take-home message?

- greatest joy, peace, healing in sacrifice; Lose self to save it.

124

Your Mind Map to Generate Theme with a Heart

2

THE EIGHT SUPPORTING PILLARS

Now that you have your four corner pillars well constructed and solidly in place, you can start building the eight supporting pillars. These, too, can be worked on in any order, but before you spend time on a particular pillar, be sure to read the related chapters in *The 12 Key Pillars of Novel Construction* so you fully understand what that pillar requires to be a strong support of your story.

Here are the eight supporting pillars you'll need to build:

- **Plot and Subplots in a String of Scenes**
- **Secondary Characters with Their Own Needs**
- **Setting with a Purpose**
- **Tension Ramped to the Max**
- **Dialog—Compressed and Essential**
- **Voice—Unique for Each Character**
- **Writing Style—Concise and Specific**
- **Motifs for Cohesion and Depth**

While the corner pillars are foundational and most essential, each of these secondary pillars is equally necessary for a successful novel. One weak pillar can compromise the integrity of a building. Two or three can cause collapse. Don't neglect any of your pillars or think some are unnecessary. Your checklists and additional brainstorming questions will help ensure you've built them well.

PILLAR #5: PLOT AND SUBPLOTS IN A STRING OF SCENES

A great, strong plot is essential for building a terrific novel. There is no excuse for a writer of any novel to sacrifice good plot for the sake of anything—art, character study, or an important message. Without plot, you have no story. Period.

But what is plot? I don't include it as one of the four essential corner pillars of novel construction. Why? Because plot is the vehicle for the other pillars. Plot is what happens in a string of scenes, one scene after the other. Plot itself isn't a pillar of novel construction, but the way scenes are constructed to unfold the plot is.

Plot is not an idea, concept, or premise. If you've developed your Concept with a Kicker, and have figured out clearly what your Conflict with High Stakes is, as well as your themes embodied in the protagonist being passionate about some outer goal pressed by inner motivation, you have the necessary framework to write a great novel. The plot, then, will be the execution of all this.

And how is that done? How do you take all those great elements you now have in place and somehow turn it into a killer novel?

By constructing scenes.

First: Read chapters 13–16 in *The 12 Key Pillars of Novel Construction* that cover Pillar #5 before you start the hard work on Plot and Subplots in a String of Scenes.

Brainstorm Key Questions

Spend some time brainstorming these questions meant to get you thinking about your plot in terms of scene structure. Before digging into the checklist questions, spend some time considering your main overarching plot and the appropriate subplots for your book. These should get your creative juices stirring. Try to freewrite your ideas.

First, think about your plot as a string of scenes laid out along a timeline. To give you an easy way to visualize this, imagine a train ride, with your starting point A as the opening scene and the end of your novel point Z. Each stop along the route is a scene. The plot is the train ride from start to finish. It is not the story; it's what gets you from point A to point Z.

A novel usually covers a limited scope of time, often under a year. It could even cover just a few hours. Unless you are writing an epic family saga or complete biography of a character's life, consider keeping that "train ride" relatively short and compact. Why? **Because a novel is about your protagonist going after one specific goal.** It's not a story of the ups and downs, successes and failures, of her life over many years. A story like that tends to lack focus and purpose, and ends up feeling like a long meaningless trip to nowhere.

So how do you determine just how much time should be covered in your novel? That's determined, again, by the protagonist and goal. The starting point as well as the end point for your story is structured around the pursuit of this goal.

If you know where along the train route your key scenes must take place, that will help you lay out your scenes and plan them in a way that is meaningful and moves the story in the right direction at the right speed.

Exercise: Grab a piece of paper (or tape a few pieces of paper end to end lengthwise) and draw your timeline. (This will be easier than trying to fit it on one page in this workbook). Mark Point A at the start of the timeline on the left. Point Z goes at the end on the right.

- The start of your timeline features your opening scenes that set up the premise and the world of your story, and showcase your protagonist and her life, needs, dreams, and ordinary world she lives in.
- Note at around the 10% mark there will be an important event or disturbance that will start your protagonist in a direction that kicks off the story and supports your premise.
- At around the 25% mark, write down the key development in your story that cements the goal for your character.
- The midpoint at 50% to the 75% mark is where your protagonist makes progress toward his goal and faces more and more obstacles along his way. The train ride gets bumpier and steeper.
- At about three-quarters along your timeline, jot down your protagonist's goal. Somewhere between the 75% and 90% mark of your novel, your protagonist is going to either reach his goal or fail. This is the climax of your novel.
- The end of your novel is the quick wrap-up of the story and loose ends.

This is a very simple sketch of basic plot structure, but it should give you a framework to play around with your main plot ideas.

Based on my concept and the goal for my protagonist, what might be the best starting point for my story and why?

My answer: Showing my protagonist in town, among his peers (including allies, antagonists, and love interest), also at his lightning survivors' meeting to set up who he is, and what his core need, fears, and guilt are all about. Show his attitude toward justice/evil/violence when he hears about the killer and his attack locally.

Your answer:

_____

_____

_____

_____

_____

What key incident might occur at the 10% mark to disturb my character's world and get him moving in a direction necessary to ultimately go after his goal? List some ideas:

My answer: The killer escapes into the mountains where hero works. A team of officers has to track him and stop him. My hero is asked (or he insists?) to be part of the team because he knows the trails and can also track (not by conventional means, as the others may think. Reveal special abilities due to his lightning strikes and a reputation for a "keen ability to track.")

Your answer:

_____

_____

_____

_____

What key event might occur at the 25% mark to establish the protagonist's goal for the book? List some ideas:

My answer: A lightning storm comes in, heightens his powers and his fear. Wants to back out, worried he'll hurt others since lightning is drawn to him. Also brings his fear up that he doesn't want to face (and his guilt)—he knows at this point this is really a battle against the lightning and his need to control it. But maybe he spots the killer and there is some altercation or attack, gunfire, someone hurt. The cops need him and he now knows without him, they will not stop the killer. So he's committed at this point to succeed, regardless of the cost.

Your answer:

_____

_____

_____

_____

_____

_____

_____

_____

What are some big obstacles and conflict that bring in high stakes for my protagonist in the middle of the book and up to the climax?

My answer: Lightning and other natural disasters, as if nature is at war with him (he believes this/takes it personally). Killer sets traps, people are injured/killed. Hero's powers run amok and cause trouble for others and also he has to deal with the thought that he is going crazy, delusional, out of control (more haunted by his past and his telekinetic powers show him things he doesn't want to see). Also others with him start suspecting his motives, distrusting/accusing, become antagonists. Lots of inner and outer conflict on the rise.

Your answer:

_____

_____

_____

_____

_____

_____

_____

_____

_____

What big climax will occur near the end of the book that paves the way for the protagonist to either reach or fail to reach his goal? How will this be the most difficult moment in this story? List some ideas:

My answer: Confrontation with the killer. High suspense and action. He has to make hard choices, with others opposing him. Moment of his greatest doubts and fears as he faces his past mistakes, let go of his need to control, face both killer and the lightning, then make the big choice to go save the hostages in danger to stop the killer but at the cost of his own life. He knows the lightning will strike him out in the open when he makes this choice but is now willing to die to be set free and also do the only right thing.

Your answer:

_____

_____

_____

_____

_____

_____

_____

_____

Breaking Down Scene Structure

The key to a great novel is building strong scenes. In a sense, scenes are the pillars that hold up your plot. No, there isn't just one way to construct a scene, just as there isn't one way to structure a novel. However, there are some very basic "rules" about scene structure that serve many successful writers well and that most great writing instructors agree on.

Scenes should "move the story along." What does that mean? That each and every scene should serve a purpose and reveal some important plot point or insight about a character.

Too often scenes ramble, are unfocused, and don't seem to have any point to them. They spread out over too much time and end up as mostly narrative summary. Our scenes need to be concise, effective, and purposeful in advancing our story. And the best way to ensure they are built well is to use a sturdy form.

The Definition of a Scene

Here's the definition of a scene by Jordan Rosenfeld in her book *Make a Scene*: "Scenes are capsules in which compelling characters undertake significant actions in a vivid and memorable way that allows the events to feel as though they are happening in real time."

So let's break her definition down:

- *Capsule*: The word capsule implies a limited, compressed period of time. Scenes start in one moment, in present action, and move forward in real time, then end—without breaking up the scene into other times, places, or POVs.

- *Compelling characters undertaking significant actions*: Scenes need to feature compelling characters, all of whom must have significant impact on the protagonist, acting as either an ally (reflection character), a romance interest, or an antagonist. All should have core needs and goals that either help or hinder the protagonist from reaching her goal. And the protagonist's actions in a scene must also be important in relation to her goal.

- *Vivid and memorable*: Use as much sensory detail in a scene to bring it to life without bogging down with too much unnecessary description. What makes a scene memorable is giving it a high moment—which reveals something essential about the characters and/or plot.

- *Happening in real time*: Backstory, long flashbacks, and excessive narration stop the present action and interrupt the pacing and flow of the scene. Author intrusion is jarring and unwelcome. Just show, don't tell, events happening as they happen. Briefly summarize what isn't important enough to show but needs to be conveyed.

When it comes to creating scenes, writers don't need to wing it, or guess or hope their scenes are structured correctly. Just as in novel construction, there are time-tested rules to ensure a powerful scene. Scenes should be like mini novels—with a beginning (starting in the middle of something happening), a middle that builds and muddles, a high moment (the point of the scene), and a strong ending (which can be hanging or resolving).

If you construct your scenes with strong "materials" and string them together in a smooth time flow, you will provide the proper framework for your plot and subplots.

A Bonus Checklist!

To help you examine each and every scene in your novel, I've created an additional bonus checklist for you. Make copies of this checklist to use for every scene, with every novel, or access it by typing this into your Internet browser and print out: **http://bit.ly/1yQEu43**. It will help you see what's missing and point out all the components needed to construct solid, tight scenes that embody the description explored above.

In addition, you'll find a helpful **scene structure template** you can copy and print out (you can also access online here: **http://dld.bz/d53zG)**. If you print double-sided, so that each template copy is one page, you can easily lay out all your "scenes" on a table and move them around to see your big story (or each "act") all at one time.

Make sure every scene has a specific point to it and features a high moment in which an important bit about character or plot is revealed—preferably before the scene is written. However, if your scenes are already written, by using the scene checklist, you can see what's missing or what needs fixing. Some scenes may need to be tossed, which can be hard to do. But if you want a strong novel, every scene must support your story, and the weak scenes, if not fixable, will weaken your structure if left in.

Additional Exercise: Grab a half dozen of your favorite novels. Randomly turn to scenes. Observe at what point in time the author begins a scene. See how she builds to a high moment then ends the scene. Figure out how much time passes during that scene. Notice how the scene is shown through the POV character and how the action is moving in real time, in the present, leaving out unessential or boring information that does not help to reveal character or plot. Take notes and gather insights that you can use in your

---

Scene Structure Checklist

Examine each of your scenes. The more you can check off the list per scene, the better!

_____ My scene has a strong opening line (hook) that grabs the reader.

_____ My scene has a beginning, middle, high point, and end (hanging or resolved).

_____ My scene is important to the plot (and I can explain exactly why and how that is).

_____ My scene helps reveal something new about the characters or plot.

_____ My scene starts in the middle of action in present time and moves forward.

_____ My scene gives a brief nod to setting through the character's POV.

_____ My scene stays in one POV the whole time and makes clear who the POV character is right away (preferably in the first two lines).

_____ My scene has dialog that has been compressed and distilled, which provides bits of important info or backstory as well as reveals character.

_____ My scene has brief bits of narrative, but not more than a few lines in one place before it switches to either internal thinking or dialog.

_____ My scene is full of sensory detail: smells, sound, textures, weather, etc.

_____ My scene clearly indicates how much time has passed since the last scene with these characters as well as the previous scene in my novel (if different).

_____ My scene evokes a rich setting to which my POV character reacts and responds.

_____ My scene's high moment advances the plot in an important way.

_____ My scene begins in a different kind of way than the scene before (usually).

_____ My scene has some element of surprise, twist, or interesting motif that makes it meaningful and helps bring across the themes of the novel.

_____ My scene is full of inner and/or outer conflict to some degree that complicates the plot and either aids or hinders my main character's attempt to reach her goal (outer motivation in the story).

_____ My scene has no dull parts; I've taken them all out! I've resisted the urge to explain!

_____ My scene has no extra words or clunky writing; I've gone through and cut as much as I could so that less is more and every word is just right and needed.

_____ My scene "moves the camera around" so that the high moment stands out and the reader is made to pay attention.

_____ My scene takes the reader where I want her to go and makes her notice what I want her to notice.

_____ My scene is infused with microtension, adding mystery by hinting at trouble, inner conflict, and secrets.

_____ My scene ends with a bang—with either some insight for the POV character, some important development, or some surprise that leaves the reader "satisfied."

_____ My scene does not tease, leave the reader confused, hint vaguely at things, or overwhelm the reader with too much information or trivial stuff.

Scene-by-Scene Outlining Template

Scene # _____

Locale:

Time of day:

Time of year:

Weather:

How much time passed since previous scene with this character?

POV character for the scene:

Scene Summary:

What main way is the story advanced? What new plot points are revealed?

What conflicts/obstacles are presented in the scene?

How does the POV character change or grow by the end of the scene?

THE high moment or key info revealed in scene:

Important backstory bits revealed in scene:

World-building or specific setting/locale details brought out:

Meaningful Subplots for Your Novel

Subplots are everywhere. We see them in the movies we watch, and they are usually in every novel we read. We may instinctively know how they work in story structure. But writers need to be careful not to throw any old subplot into a story in the hope that it will just add some interest. If you keep in mind that everything that goes into your novel must serve the advancement and complication of the main plot, you will fare well.

What do I mean by "serve the advancement" of the main plot? This brings us back to our four support corner pillars. The main plot is all about a protagonist going after a goal in the midst of conflict and high stakes. That's the essence of the main plot's purpose—to be a vehicle for this character and her objective in the story.

So, if you keep in mind that any subplots (additional plotlines) you create should add to the main plot in a meaningful way, that can help you come up with some interesting and helpful subplots.

Subplots can involve your protagonist and/or your secondary characters. The best purpose for subplots is to enrich, deepen, and help advance the main plot and reveal character motivation. So with every subplot you add in (and often, the more the better), utilizing any number of secondary characters, find a way for each additional story line to be a complication.

For whom? Ultimately, for your protagonist. For, even if the subplot is about another character, the impact of what that character is going through has to affect your protagonist.

Plot Layers That Mimic Real Life

We want our characters to have lives that feel real and similar to our own. Novels should be portraying a slice of real life (but just more interesting, we hope). Our lives are multilayered with different objectives or goals, and if you look at your life in these terms, you can identify numerous goals you are pursuing each day, year in and year out, each differing in importance.

By making sure all the secondary plots tie in, enhance, and, most importantly, complicate the main plot concerning the protagonist going after his visible goal, you will be working with strong construction materials.

Don't throw random subplots into your novel just for filler or because you think they are neat ideas. They really must serve a purpose in your story. Sure, make some of them entertaining, even providing comic relief. Subplots really help to bring out your characters and all their issues, and they help make your characters clash, which, to me, is the best reason for layering plots.

Plots A, B, and C

Think about your main plot as Plot A. Then try to come up with another plot thread a little less important, and maybe more immediate, that your character needs to pay attention to in the story. That is Plot B. Choose something a little mundane or bothersome for Plot C. You can have more than one Plot B or C for your protagonist. And your secondary characters can also have these similar layers. Sometimes the more subplots, the better—if they all help to support and advance your main plot.

Your Protagonist:

What is your main plot about (Plot A)? State in one concise sentence that highlights your protagonist's goal:

My answer: My hero chases a killer in the mountains in order to stop him and keep others safe.

Your answer:

_____

_____

_____

What other important things can my protagonist be concerned about in her daily life that impacts her ability to go after her core need or goal (Plot B)? Freewrite some ideas:

My answer: His mental and physical health due to his lightning strikes and the toll it's taken on him. This is just as important as the visible plot so is almost another Plot A. Some secondary plots might be dealing with the guilt he's plagued with—conflict between him and his father over the incident that he's to blame for (I'm thinking now his twin brother died when they were teens because of being out on a lake during a lightning storm), and monetary issues (maybe he's dealing with losing his house). Could have romance trouble too.

Your answer:

_____

_____

_____

_____

_____

_____

What minor irritation can be upending her life that causes her additional stress (Plot C)? Try to come up with at least five ideas:

My answer: Sick dog, annoying neighbor, irritating work partner (who might also be on the hunt), a nagging health issue (resulting from a previous lightning strike, like migraines or a pain in his knee that flares up and he's trying to medicate).

Your answer:

_____

_____

_____

_____

_____

Secondary Characters:

What plot goal can one or more of your *ally* characters have in the novel (Plot A)? [If you haven't developed your secondary characters yet, come back to this later after you've done so.]

My answer: My protagonist's best friend could be dealing with very difficult health issues due to being struck by lightning, which my hero could be involved with (helping out). This ally character's goal could be to get proper medical treatment, which has been impossible and resulting in lots of pain. Another ally's goal could be to get the hero to marry her (if I want a love interest). The protagonist's coworker in this crucible with the hero could have a goal of retiring without getting killed and so endangers the others.

Your answer:

_____

_____

_____

_____

_____

_____

_____

Now, explain why and how these possible subplots might support and enhance your main plot:

My answer: My hero can worry over the friend with health problems (ally might die if hero doesn't do something soon), and the pressure of this, and from the woman in love with him (he can't deal with loving anyone right now, so inner conflict, as he doesn't want to hurt her either). The coworker with a selfish agenda can really mess up his efforts and cause great conflict, tension, and complications by sabotaging hero (as antagonist) while they're tracking the killer.

Your answer:

_____

_____

_____

_____

_____

_____

_____

_____

_____

_____

What less important plot goal can you give your ally characters (Plot B)?

My answer: Best friend could lose his car and need transportation. Love interest could have ex harassing her and she's trying to get him off her back (custody?).

Your answer:

_____

_____

_____

What plot goal can one or more of your *nemesis* characters have in the novel (Plot A)? [If you haven't developed your secondary characters yet, come back to this later after you've done so.]

My answer: The coworker with his selfish agenda could be suffering from borderline nervous breakdown and just pushing to make it to retirement. The killer of course has the goal of getting away and succeeding at his attempt to kill or pull off a terrorist attack.

Your answer:

_____

_____

_____

_____

_____

_____

Now, explain why and how these possible subplots might support and enhance your main plot:

My answer: Will add lots of emotional pressure and added danger to the situation as he goes after killer. Maybe coworker despises hero (because he's honorable) and will create lots of tension as he disagrees with methods and hero's decisions (subordinate? Resentful because hero has his higher status and he was passed over for promotion?). Coworker may purposely endanger hero's life.

Your answer:

_____

_____

_____

_____

_____

_____

What less important goal can you give the nemesis characters (Plot B)?

My answer: Coworker could just want to ditch and get out alive. Get hero to admit something he's done wrong or apologize. He may want to find a get-rich-quick scheme to pay off his gambling debts.

Your answer:

_____

_____

_____

What plot goal can your *romance* character have in the novel (Plot A), if you are including such a character? [If you haven't developed your secondary characters yet, come back to this later after you've done so.]

My answer: Aside from wanting to win the hero's heart, she could want a family or a new job. She might be considering moving away for work, which makes her put pressure on hero to commit to her.

Your answer:

_____

_____

_____

Now, explain why and how these possible subplots might support and enhance your main plot:

My answer: Again, puts pressure on hero and might get him considering moving away and not facing his fear or giving up the work he loves. Inner conflict. May interfere with his abilities and concentration as he goes after his goals. May outwardly sabotage his efforts.

Your answer:

_____

_____

_____

_____

_____

_____

What less important plot goal can you give your romance character (Plot B)?

My answer: She could be struggling with an ex, dealing with child support, a family member with a health issue (maybe she met hero through that family member being in same lightning survivor's group or she could also be a victim of lightning and sometimes acts as antagonist to him because of her own fears).

Your answer:

_____

_____

_____

_____

_____

_____

Now, think about the end of your novel. Does your protagonist reach her goal? Do the other characters reach their goals? Explain how all these goals fit together by the end of your story and how they impact the protagonist:

My answer: Hero reaches his goals to stop killer and face down his fears and conquer them. Through this liberation, he might also decide he can now love, and so his girlfriend would get her goal of winning him. His coworker should die due to his bad attitude (just deserts), and his best friend would get the help he needs through hero, who gets some big reward $$?

Your answer:

_____

_____

_____

_____

_____

_____

_____

_____

_____

_____

After playing around with all these ideas, which plot threads seem to you to be the best and strongest to develop and integrate into your novel?

_____

_____

_____

_____

_____

_____

_____

Additional exercise: Choose five novels you love, then jot down the subplots you see presented. Note the A, B, and C types of plots for the protagonist and the secondary characters. Note how these subplots help support and enhance the main plot (or not). How does this examination help you come up with your plot and subplots?

Inspection Checklist #5

Plot and Subplots in a String of Scenes

Here are the sets of questions and exercises on your inspection checklist, and more. Take time to think these through and answer them. If you haven't yet come up with the solid answers you need for some of these questions, leave them blank and come back to them later.

Question Set #1:

Take the time to look at each of your scenes. Does each scene have a beginning, middle, high point, and ending? Choose your weakest scene and state what the high point (important moment) is:

_____

_____

_____

If you don't have a high moment or some new plot point or character insight for that scene, come up with some ideas:

_____

_____

_____

_____

_____

Where might you start that scene in the middle of action, not long before the high moment? Tell what your character could be already doing:

_____

_____

_____

_____

Ask: How might my character change in this scene? How does he see things a bit differently by the end of the scene?

_____

_____

_____

_____

How might you end the scene in a way that makes the reader want to keep reading? What feeling are you trying to leave with the reader?

_____

_____

_____

_____

_____

Do this process with all your weak scenes—the ones that fail to "pass" the scene checklist provided earlier in this chapter.

Question Set #2:

Does every scene advance your main plot by revealing new, important info about character or the plot or by adding complications or obstacles for your main character in reaching her goal?

Pick your weakest scene and explain how it advances the plot (or how you might rework it so it does):

_____

_____

_____

_____

_____

Come up with some possible ways to complicate things for your character(s) in this weak scene:

_____

_____

_____

_____

_____

_____

Do this process with all your weak scenes—the ones that fail to "pass" the scene checklist provided earlier in this chapter.

Question Set #3:

Does every scene have an opening hook that grabs the reader? A great last line that leaves the scene hanging or wraps it up just right?

Pick your weakest scene and come up with a gripping opening hook:

_____

_____

_____

_____

_____

Come up with some possible last lines, surprises, or twists in this weak scene:

_____

_____

_____

_____

_____

_____

_____

Do this process with all your weak scenes—the ones that fail to "pass" the scene checklist provided earlier in this chapter.

Question Set #4:

Does every scene clearly set up where, when, and who is the focus of the scene right away?

Pick your weakest scene and create a first paragraph that sets up the place, time, and POV character:

_____

_____

_____

_____

_____

How will you show in this weak scene how much time has passed since the prior scene?

_____

_____

_____

_____

_____

_____

Do this process with all your weak scenes—the ones that fail to "pass" the scene checklist provided earlier in this chapter.

Question Set #5:

Does every scene start in the middle of something happening? Have you deleted all the boring, nonessential action and words that make your scenes drag?

Pick your weakest scene and describe how you might start in the middle of action, without explaining or using long passages of narrative:

_____

_____

_____

_____

_____

_____

What boring bits can you take out or rewrite that bog down your scene?

_____

_____

_____

_____

_____

Do this process with all your weak scenes—the ones that fail to "pass" the scene checklist provided earlier in this chapter.

Question #6:

Sum up your main plot in one sentence. Does it clearly show your protagonist's visible goal for the novel as well as the central conflict? Rework it until your plot objective is clear.

_____

_____

_____

Question Set #7:

What are the two main subplots for your protagonist (Plot B and C)? In what ways do they complicate the main plot?

_____

_____

_____

_____

_____

Enrich your themes?

_____

_____

_____

_____

Question Set #8:

What are the subplots you've created for two of your secondary characters? [Come back to this later if you haven't developed your secondary characters yet.]

_____

_____

_____

_____

_____

In what ways do they complicate the main plot and showcase your theme?

_____

_____

_____

Help or hinder your protagonist?

_____

_____

_____

Question #9:

List three ways your subplots bring out your themes:

_____

_____

_____

_____

_____

_____

_____

Can you find a way in five scenes to bring out the theme even more? Note how you'll do this:

_____

_____

_____

_____

_____

_____

_____

_____

_____

Question #10:

Describe a subplot you have or might create that has a secondary character's goal clashing with your protagonist's goal:

_____

_____

_____

_____

How could you make it worse, with greater consequences?

_____

_____

_____

_____

Question Set #11:

What minor subplot (Plot C) do you have for your protagonist?

_____

_____

_____

_____

_____

How might you aggravate the situation so that it pushes your character over the edge?

_____

_____

_____

_____

Question Set #12:

Find your three weakest scenes and list, briefly, what happens in each:

_____

_____

_____

_____

_____

_____

_____

_____

_____

_____

How can you salvage these by infusing a twist, an important high moment, a revelation or insight for your character?

_____

_____

_____

_____

_____

_____

_____

_____

_____

_____

Write a one-paragraph summary of your novel highlighting Plot and Subplots in a String of Scenes:

_____

_____

_____

_____

_____

My Mind Map to Generate Plot and Subplots

Hero's B+C plots

- Physical issues from lightning (mental too)

- dealing with father + blame

- trying to help lightning survivors

- struggling with bills / losing his house

- problems w/ girlfriend because he cant work out his inner problems

main plot arc

Hero dealing with his problems joins team to chase after a killer who flees to the mountain. Hero has to stop killer amid increasing dangers + inner conflict. Rising stakes - climax is big confrontation + test.

Plot A visible goal

Stop killer
save hostages

Developments for subplots

- lots of natural disasters (slides, quakes, fires)

- worsening storm

- opposition from team members

- lose house, father disowns him (emotional stresses)

- hostages taken people hurt / killed

- animal attacks?

- hero's powers increase + make him crazy

- lightning chasing him, harder for hero to reach goal.

Plot and Subplots

Secondary characters' plots and goals

- Ally friend dying or in need of lots of care. Hero may need to step up help.

- Girlfriend wants hero to marry her. She's after a better job + wants to move, which puts pressure on hero.

- antagonist coworker's goal to save himself in hostage situation creates problems + conflict + sets in hero's way to his goal

- killer, of course has his goal to reach (terrorist attack? Needs girlfriend's knowledge?)

Your Mind Map to Generate Plot and Subplots

PILLAR #6: SECONDARY CHARACTERS
WITH THEIR OWN NEEDS

The importance of secondary characters in your novel cannot be overemphasized. They are crucial to your story—unless you are writing about a protagonist in isolation, which is a unique kind of story. And novels about one person off alone are challenging to write because of the dearth of a "supporting cast."

Having other characters in your novel makes it much easier to construct a strong story. Why? Because these characters provide support and opposition to your protagonist as he goes after his goal for the book. If you keep this in mind, you will create additional characters that will either help or hinder your protagonist.

All too often, as what happens with subplots, secondary characters are thrown into a novel without much thought or purpose. This is a bad thing. Just as with every element in your story, your secondary characters have to serve very specific purposes. They should be created each for a reason, to play a key part in the story.

Don't throw characters in for random drama or laughs without giving thought to the bigger picture. You may make it appear as if a lot is happening, when actually all these characters do is clutter and distract from the main story.

What these characters do in your story is important, but who they are is even more vital. Relationships are at the heart of your story, so think about creating characters that play key roles in affecting your protagonist and impacting his character arc, while showing their own arc as well.

First: Read chapters 17–19 in *The 12 Key Pillars of Novel Construction* that cover Pillar #6 before you start the hard work on Secondary Characters with Their Own Needs.

Brainstorm Key Questions

Spend some time brainstorming these questions meant to get you thinking about your secondary characters. Before digging into the checklist questions, spend some time thinking about what types of characters might populate your story and why. In the previous chapter, there are questions pertaining to your secondary characters' goals, so be sure to work on those as you develop your supportive cast.

What kind of character would be the best ally for my protagonist and why?

My answer: His closest ally will be an older man from his lightning survivors' group because this guy has been through what the hero's been through, and he can be a mirror/reflection to the hero to help him see his fears and guilt and give him advice on what he needs to do. This man would be a surrogate father for hero because hero's own father blames him for the accident years ago.

Your answer:

_____

_____

_____

_____

_____

What kind of character would be the best antagonist for my protagonist and why?

My answer: Coworker who is another ranger, but one who is a close-minded redneck who only cares about himself. He's the best choice because he'll be on the hunt for the killer with the hero and will sabotage and endanger, which raises stakes. Also he opposes hero on all thematic issues and is vocal about that.

Your answer:

_____

_____

_____

_____

_____

Will you have a romance character in your novel? If so, what's he/she like? If not, why not? Is there a possibility your story could use one?

My answer: Hero has girlfriend but he can't commit and brings all his issues to the relationship, which is taxing it. She loves and believes in him but is getting sick of his problems and obsession with lightning. She isn't very patient and is very ambitious.

Your answer:

_____

_____

_____

_____

If your novel does feature a romance character, how might his/her core needs clash with your protagonist's?

My answer: Her core need might be to succeed in her career, which would press her to want/need to move to a different city. That puts pressure on hero to commit and consider leaving a place and life he loves (maybe she wants to move to NY or someplace where there is no wilderness nearby, which he thrives on and needs). She also may think the move would be good for him.

Your answer:

_____

_____

_____

_____

_____

_____

What other secondary characters might you populate your novel with and why? How will they help or hinder the protagonist reaching his goal?

My answer: Others in the survivors' group could provide a colorful cast of characters that hero is trying to help. His father would be an important one because he blames hero for the brother's death and exacerbates the hero's guilt and pain. Father creates huge emotional conflict for hero, and by end of book, there can be healing between them when hero comes into his "essence" and finds the answers and healing he needs.

Your answer:

_____

_____

_____

_____

_____

_____

_____

_____

_____

_____

Character Development

(print out copies and use for all your characters)

Name of character:

_____

Basic physical description:

_____

_____

Most noticeable physical attribute:

_____

Age, body type, build:

_____

_____

Birthplace and where he/she grew up:

_____

_____

Educational background:

_____

_____

First impression most have of her/him:

_____

_____

Dominant personality traits:

_____

_____

Hobby or main interest:

_____

_____

Best friend and why:

_____

_____

Main opponent and why:

_____

_____

Weakest character trait:

_____

_____

Strongest character trait:

_____

_____

Things he/she is passionate about:

_____

_____

Core need:

_____

_____

What he/she will do if that need isn't met:

_____

_____

Driven by what motivation:

_____

_____

Deepest fear:

_____

_____

Secret he/she would never tell anyone:

_____

_____

What he/she wants more than anything else in life right now:

_____

_____

Most painful past experience:

_____

_____

Greatest/most painful past loss:

_____

_____

The lie he/she believes about self (due to past experience):

_____

_____

The lie he/she believes about others or the world:

_____

_____

What he she does to not face her/his fears:

_____

_____

What kind of work/vocation? Why?

_____

_____

Feelings about parents:

_____

_____

Feelings about siblings:

_____

_____

Main way he/she changes in the novel—elaborate:

_____

_____

_____

_____

_____

Inspection Checklist #6

Secondary Characters with Their Own Needs

Here are the sets of questions and exercises on your inspection checklist, and more. Take time to think these through and answer them. If you haven't yet come up with the solid answers you need for some of these questions, leave them blank and come back to them later.

Question #1:

Do you have at least 3 supporting characters that play key roles and are there to either help or hinder the main character? List how they do this in the story.

_____

_____

_____

_____

_____

_____

_____

_____

_____

_____

Question #2:

List each of their core needs, goals, greatest fear, and deepest desire.
How do these create conflict or support for your protagonist?

_____

_____

_____

_____

_____

_____

_____

_____

_____

_____

_____

_____

_____

_____

_____

_____

_____

_____

_____

Question #3:

Can you think of a key scene to put in your novel in which your most supportive ally opposes your protagonist regarding her goal? Describe it:

_____

_____

_____

_____

_____

_____

_____

_____

_____

Question Set #4:

Who is the primary reflection character/ally for your protagonist? What key moment is in your novel that showcases his support?

_____

_____

_____

_____

Question Set #5:

Who is the primary antagonist in your novel? What key moment showcases the conflict and issue between him and your protagonist?

_____

_____

_____

_____

_____

_____

_____

Question #6:

What are three ways or moments in which you show your antagonist(s) as human, vulnerable, almost sympathetic?

_____

_____

_____

_____

_____

_____

Question Set #7:

In what big way do your secondary characters create Conflict with High Stakes for your protagonist? Can you make the conflict and stakes bigger? Describe how:

_____

_____

_____

_____

_____

_____

_____

_____

_____

Question #8:

What is the big moment in which the most supportive ally helps the protagonist change and/or reach her visible goal in or right before the climax?

_____

_____

_____

_____

_____

_____

_____

_____

_____

Question #9:

How do the A and B plots and subplots you developed for each of your secondary characters help/hinder the protagonist's goal?

_____

_____

_____

_____

_____

_____

_____

_____

_____

_____

_____

Question #10:

In what ways do you use the secondary characters to bring out the themes in your novel? Can you come up with at least three key scenes?

_____

_____

_____

_____

_____

_____

_____

_____

_____

_____

_____

Question #11:

Do you have a romance character and element in your novel? List the key factor or development in 6-12 scenes (1 line each) that shows how the relationship gradually develops with conflict and connection:

_____

_____

_____

_____

_____

_____

_____

_____

_____

_____

_____

_____

Question #12:

How does the romance character act as a reflection for your protagonist?
Lists three key moments when he/she helps the protagonist see his/her
true self:

_____

_____

_____

_____

_____

_____

_____

_____

Write a one-paragraph summary of your novel highlighting Secondary Characters with Their Own Needs:

_____

_____

_____

_____

_____

_____

_____

_____

_____

Additional Exercise: Make a list of all your secondary characters. Give each one a quirk (physical or something they say), a unique gesture or nervous habit, an odd hobby or interest. Find places in your novel to add these in to make your characters unique and intriguing.

My Mind Map to Generate Secondary Characters

Love interest

Girlfriend — been together awhile. Knows hero from childhood so is aware of the death of brother. Loves hero but has her own goal (career — maybe fashion designer) so puts pressure on hero to move. She's a good match for him but believes he should leave his problems behind instead of face them.

Best friend

old guy in survivors' group really likes hero. They've helped each other a lot. He's Southern, funny, generous. Hero really admires his blunt honesty + the way the guy forces him to be honest + courageous with himself + fears.

Secondary Characters

other allies

· friends in the survivors' group

· other coworkers + those on the team going after killer

· neighbor who doesn't want hero to lose his house

· possibly an old school friend who also knew hero's brother + who instilled love of wilderness in hero (and isn't afraid of lightning).

antagonists

- killer (obvious) but it's not personal

- lightning — very personal + personified (best if hero thinks lightning is "out to get him," when in actuality it's' helping him see + face "light" of truth.

— coworker jerk who gets in the way + selfishly tries to save himself. Causes death + destruction due to his selfishness + carelessness

— father — who has never forgiven him

Your Mind Map to Generate Secondary Characters

PILLAR #7: SETTING WITH A PURPOSE

Setting serves a number of very powerful, key functions in a novel's scenes, and that's why it's an essential pillar of novel construction. Without setting, how can you have a story?

Often writers seem so intent on conveying dialog or explaining about the characters that they forget (or think it is unimportant) to mention where their characters just happen to be.

And that's a shame, because writers like that are missing out on a great opportunity to bring a novel to life. The more real a place is to readers, the easier they can be transported there to experience the story.

You may feel that if you are not writing a fantasy novel, you don't have to "build your world." But you do. You might ask, why would you need to "build" New York City, for example, when most people know a lot about that city from TV, movies, news, and even personal experience?

The answer circles back again to the point that your novel is shown through the eyes of the POV characters. This means that in every scene, someone is experiencing the place they are in as the plot develops.

The more you can have the setting of each scene affect and impact your characters in some way, the more real and personal your story will feel. If setting isn't all that important to your concept and plot, spend some time thinking about how to make it so. Consider changing the locale your novel takes place in to one with greater purpose for your story.

First: Read chapters 20–21 in *The 12 Key Pillars of Novel Construction* that cover Pillar #7 before you start the hard work on Setting with a Purpose.

Brainstorm Key Questions

Spend some time brainstorming these questions meant to get you thinking about overall setting or locale for your novel, as well as the individual scene settings. Before digging into the checklist questions, spend some time thinking about what types of settings you might have in your story and why.

First consideration is the *overall locale* of your novel's setting, which may be one place, like a small town, or have an international hodgepodge of locales, such as in Ludlum's Bourne series. It may be that your premise requires a very specific location, but if not, take the time to think about your concept and the protagonist's goal, and think of places to set your characters so they can provide as much interest, potential for conflict, and utility for your story. And of course it has to be a place that works for your protagonist's background and personality.

What locale have I chosen for my novel's overall setting and why?

My answer: In general, I chose mountains because my protagonist needs to be in a place where he can best confront lightning, and I've given him a vocation and passion (for the wilderness) that puts him best in conflict. Since part of the story will be in a city so he has more interaction with "real life," I'll pick Washington State because I need a Western mountain—Mt. Rainier (least lightning)—close to a city (Seattle). A big mountain like this affords lots of opportunity for natural disasters. It's also feasible to have volcanic activity (not that far from Mt. St. Helens that erupted).

Your answer:

_____

_____

_____

_____

_____

_____

_____

_____

_____

What are some other possible locales that might work, and how might they be better or worse?

My answer: I could set this somewhere else in the US, in the Rockies or other mountains. I want him to get as far from the South as possible (where he previously worked and where lightning strikes are highest), but because I need him close enough to a city to have an impacting possible terrorist threat and have the highest public stakes, I need a big mountain near a big city. Denver is possible (65 miles to Estes Park; Seattle is 54 miles from Mt. Rainier). Either should work for my plot needs. Not too many high mountains close to big urban areas.

Your answer:

_____

_____

_____

_____

_____

_____

_____

_____

How is the locale I've chosen the best place to showcase the protagonist's goal and provide the most conflict and high stakes?

My answer: By choosing a mountain close to a high-population urban area, more people can be in danger from the terrorist. My hero's goal is to stop the killer as he flees into the mountains, which is hero's "domain" and showcases both his talents and training as well as his special powers that the lightning gave him. A big treacherous mountain with dangers allows high stakes for him and those with him. He will have to rely mostly on himself in the general isolation in the mountain, which makes him also face down his inner fears and thus provides that strong inner conflict. If some of the area triggers strong memories of his brother's death, it will amplify his guilt and cause stress.

Your answer:

_____

_____

_____

_____

_____

_____

_____

Next consideration is *the individual scenes* in your book. If you are trying to show a character's well-rounded life, you will want a number of different locales showcasing his job, his family, his hobbies, where he hangs out with his friends. Don't choose random settings for no apparent reason as a backdrop for your story. Or default to the same setting over and over. That means missing out on a very useful structural component for a story. Setting is so powerful in our lives, and it can—and should—be in the lives of our characters.

What are some of the key settings I feature in my novel and why are they good choices?

My answer: Aside from the bulk of the story set in the mountain, scenes in the city will include where he meets with the lightning survivors, the main park office where he interacts with coworkers, his father's home (so he can have conflict with Dad), a hospital or ward when his best friend is confined due to lightning injury, girlfriend's hangout or work (develop that).

Your answer:

_____

_____

_____

_____

_____

_____

_____

_____

_____

What three places are significant to my protagonist? Why? What important things will happen there?

My answer: At his survivors' meeting he will see more suffering to ramp up his anger at lightning and also see how he's odd (with his powers), which alienates him too. At his city office he can have a big confrontation with the coworker/antagonist who will be on the team after the killer (shows the relationship dynamics with him and those he works with). An abandoned lookout tower atop the mountain where he'll have the big confrontation with the terrorist who has taken some of his group hostage at the climax of the novel (where he faces down lightning and his fears).

Your answer:

_____

_____

_____

_____

_____

_____

_____

_____

Where might my protagonist hang out with friends? To be alone? What place holds the most pain or memories?

My answer: At or around the meeting hall with the lightning survivors since he's dedicated to helping others (maybe he leads this group). He has a special place in the mountain where he goes to be alone, which reminds him of where his brother died (a similar-looking lake). He does this to relive the pain and wallow in his guilt. His father's house also holds painful memories—mementos and photos of his brother. He might also frequent a park where he meets with his best friend/ally who is the injured lightning survivor (they may have a regular time they walk together, which can show some of the bigger setting of the city).

Your answer:

_____

_____

_____

_____

_____

_____

Think of a place in your past that is highly emotionally charged for you, where something important took place. What place can you create for your protagonist that has similar emotional impact?

My answer: Where I went to summer camp high up in the Sierra Mountains. I spent parts of eight summers there (city girl from LA exposed to nature) and learned to backpack and ride river rapids. Very emotionally charged to me because it instilled my love for the mountains and the wilderness. Many powerful moments sitting beside rivers and cresting mountain peaks, feeling a part of the world and nature and being humbled and awed by the beauty of the world. My hero can have these intense moments in which he is awed by nature and the power/potential inherent there, which wars with his fears from his terrifying encounters with lightning. He struggles with his destiny and purpose in life, with setting inspiring such deep reflection and inner conflict.

Your answer:

_____

_____

_____

_____

_____

_____

_____

_____

List three places where the most important moments will take place in your story. Why did you choose these? Can you think of better ones?

My answer: The climax will be at the top of the mountain for the best confrontation with lightning, and where the lookout tower is. Allows a big dramatic climax and also a shelter where the killer can hide and hold hostages. For his big mirror/reflection moment maybe at his father's house, where all his guilt memories flood him, at the moment he has to make a choice to act or not (which would have to be a bit early in the book). I'd like one big important scene in the city at the survivors' meeting to allow for a lot of character interaction and info about lightning, with ally friend who makes him face his fears (maybe hero confesses or demonstrates his secret abilities?). Or with girlfriend?

Your answer:

_____

_____

_____

_____

_____

_____

_____

_____

Briefly, list what the most important feature of your primary location is and how it impacts your protagonist and his goal:

My answer: The mountain peak is the most important feature because he stands atop the world and confronts lightning and the killer. It's exposed, making him (and others) vulnerable, reducing all his needs and fears and goals to a stark, clear confrontation.

Your answer:

_____

_____

_____

_____

Inspection Checklist #7

Setting with a Purpose

Here are the sets of questions and exercises on your inspection checklist, and more. Take time to think these through and answer them. If you haven't yet come up with the solid answers you need for some of these questions, leave them blank and come back to them later.

Question Set #1:

Have you deliberately chosen a primary setting/locale for your novel? Why this place and not another?

_____

_____

_____

_____

_____

What other setting or locale might work or be even better? Try to list three possible settings and give reasons for your choices:

_____

_____

_____

_____

_____

Question #2:

For every scene, have you asked: "Is this the best setting I can put my characters in?" Pick three scenes that could use a stronger setting and list some better possibles here:

_____

_____

_____

_____

_____

_____

_____

Question Set #3:

What is your main character's connection with the primary settings in your novel?

_____

_____

_____

_____

_____

_____

Can you make the emotions deeper and more meaningful? How?

_____

_____

_____

_____

_____

_____

_____

Question Set #4:

What important past events can you come up with that tie three of your characters to your settings?

_____

_____

_____

_____

_____

_____

_____

_____

_____

How might you bring some of that backstory into your novel scenes?

_____

_____

_____

_____

_____

_____

_____

_____

Question Set #5:

How many "boring" settings do you have in which characters stand or sit around and talk? (yes, go find and count them!) How many can you change to make the setting more interesting? Explain how you'll do this:

_____

_____

_____

_____

_____

_____

_____

Question #6:

In what ways can you significantly change the way your protagonist feels about the setting by what happens to her in your story?

_____

_____

_____

_____

_____

_____

_____

Question Set #7:

What unusual things can you have your protagonist notice about the various settings she is in, colored by her mood and what is happening in the story?

_____

_____

_____

_____

_____

Can you think of a motif that could tie into this feeling/setting connection? Something that represents her inner motivation or core need? A theme in your book?

_____

_____

_____

_____

_____

_____

_____

_____

Question Set #8:

Go through your scenes and check: Have you clearly established the weather, time of day, time of year? Does the weather fit the mood or purpose of each scene? Pick some scenes in which you could alter the weather or time of day to make the scene more tense or impacting and describe how and why you will change them:

_____

_____

_____

_____

_____

_____

_____

_____

Question Set #9:

Do you establish your setting right away in every scene and through the POV character's eyes? Check that. Do you give strong sensory details? List five scenes that need work, and then get to work on them:

_____

_____

_____

_____

_____

Question Set #10:

Pick one place that has special significance for your protagonist. What happened there? How does she feel there?

_____

_____

_____

_____

_____

Can you put her there in important moments in your story? Which moments? How will the setting affect her thoughts, choices, or mood?

_____

_____

_____

_____

_____

_____

_____

_____

_____

Question Set #11:

Can you create a place/locale in your story that triggers your protagonist to feel sad? Where is this and why does she feel sad?

_____

_____

_____

_____

_____

_____

How about afraid? Nostalgic? Reflective? Angry? Regretful? Guilty?

_____

_____

_____

_____

_____

_____

_____

_____

_____

_____

Question #12:

Can you come up with a significant moment in the climax and/or ending of your book that shows strong connection between your protagonist and the setting? Tell what happens:

_____

_____

_____

_____

_____

Write a one-paragraph summary of your novel highlighting Setting with a Purpose:

_____

_____

_____

_____

_____

_____

_____

Additional Exercise: Come up with three specific locales in the primary setting you've chosen for your novel that have some local and/or historical significance. Think of something iconic that characterizes that place, such as the Statue of Liberty in New York or The Tower of London. Even if your novel is set in a "nothing" small town, create something of meaning to the residents of this town. Now think how you can connect your themes to these locales. Think how you might come up with a motif that can symbolize your theme. Have your protagonist "relate" to a bit of history that occurred there, and tie in with his core need and/or goal for the book. This is a great way to bring your specific setting to life in a powerful way in your novel.

My Mind Map to Generate Setting with a Purpose

overall setting

Mountains - on trails,
bushwacking, at the
peak. Must be close
to a big city with
large population for
high stakes

Seattle - will have
rain + good choice
due to feasible volcano
+ earthquake activity
(Mt. Rainier close to Mt.
St. Helens)

Denver also good choice.
~~Potential~~ for snow in city,
high elevations

other settings
for ~~scenes~~

Setting with
a Purpose

Scenes
in the
mountains

- meetings in the
heart of the city with
survivors' group can
showcase the city +
reveal what hero loves
+ hates about it. Will
contain good + painful memories.

- father's house outside town
in foothills - pain associated
(photos/mementos of brother)
+ tension with father. Good
memories too of childhood
with brother in wilderness
beyond his backyard.

- brother's grave? memories and
backstory there

- work office in city (ranger HQ?)
to show him in his vocation +
how he interacts with coworkers

- girlfriend's work or nearby where
they meet (park?) + talk.

- on the trails
as disaster strikes

- open high areas
where lightning
strikes

- a lake that either
is similar to or IS
the lake where his
brother died (Hero
took him out in a
boat + lightning hit,
caused brother to drown)

- Lookout tower
where big climax
+ confrontation with
killer takes place.
Hostages are in there

210

Your Mind Map to Generate Setting with a Purpose

PILLAR #8: TENSION RAMPED TO THE MAX

Novels need to be infused with tension, but writers often have no idea what kind of tension is needed or how to create it.

There are two aspects of tension novelists need to be aware of. There is the tension the characters feel as individuals and then there is the overall tension in the story. Don't confuse action with tension. Don't confuse high drama and high stakes with tension. You can have the most exciting plot elements in the world—with car chase scenes and buildings blowing up and the threat of the end of the world and still completely lack any tension—as far as the reader is concerned.

So while you may be writing about tense things that should make people feel tense, or you are showing characters under stress, that doesn't necessarily equate to your book's tension. *Which is to say that the tension a writer should be aiming for is something other than making readers feeling uptight or worried.*

What we as writers want is tension *in the reader*. And that kind of tension is not dependent on what kind of action is going on in a story. Even the most subdued, quiet, nothing-seems-to-be-happening scene can have tension ramped to the max.

No, this doesn't mean we want our readers to be stressed-out—although if you are writing intense suspense, that probably is exactly your aim. The kind of tension we want readers to feel is a sense of heightened anticipation, interest, curiosity, excitement. This is a good kind of tension. In other words, we want readers to care so much about what is going on that they are uncomfortable. And when someone is uncomfortable, they want to resolve whatever it is to the point at which they can again feel comfortable.

First: Read chapter 22 in *The 12 Key Pillars of Novel Construction* that covers Pillar #8 before you start the hard work on Ramping Tension to the Max.

Brainstorm Key Questions

Spend some time brainstorming these questions meant to get you thinking about the tension in your novel. You want two types of tension in your novel: the tension created by the story and the tension your characters are feeling, which manifests in inner conflict and outer conflict.

Conflict creates tension for your characters, which readers will feel if you immerse them into the emotions and thoughts of those characters. By showing your characters "tense" instead of telling about it (narrative summary), you can ensure your readers will feel that tension.

The secret to great tension is great characters with a lot of inner conflict, and that isn't easy to sum up simply using a workbook. Outer conflict adds tension too, and that's important, but if readers don't care about what happens to your characters, that tension will be lacking, and the pacing of your scenes will drag.

What is the primary *outer* conflict my protagonist faces in the novel and why will this create a lot of tension?

My answer: The primary outer tension is generated by the visible plot of the hero and his team going after the killer in the mountains. The killer has weapons and is dangerous, and the hero has his weapons (both actual and psychic/physical) to face the killer. By having scenes with lots of danger from this situation as well as the natural threats occurring around them, my hero will have plenty of outer conflict. Conflict heightens when killer grabs and takes some characters hostage.

Your answer:

_____

_____

_____

_____

_____

_____

_____

_____

What is the primary _inner_ conflict my protagonist faces in the novel and why will this create a lot of tension?

My answer: My hero is dealing with a ton of inner conflict that will create tension. The primary issue is his fear and anger at lightning, which acts as a direct nemesis character for him. He deals with his strange powers, which causes him physical pain and emotional grief, by making him feel cursed and as if he is losing his mind. The mental confusion and turmoil adds great tension. In addition, his core need to expiate his guilt over his brother's death torments him and is exacerbated by the locale in which he chases down the killer. This inner conflict affects those he's around and gets some to doubt him and turn on him.

Your answer:

_____

_____

_____

_____

_____

_____

_____

_____

What are some additional components of inner and outer conflict in my novel that will create tension?

My answer: Additional outer conflict will be between the team members going after the killer, as they have different agendas, needs, and fears, with one primary antagonist disagreeing and even sabotaging the hero. Raised stakes when the killer takes hostages and possibly kills and hurts some of the team. The weather and increasing natural disasters (caused in part by the heightening of hero's powers, and/or the lightning drawn to him) adds more outer conflict. If a close friend (his love interest?) turns against him or is put in danger (maybe she is one of the hostages, a ranger too?) that can add conflict. His father can admit he blames hero for the brother's death—adds to hero's guilt.

Your answer:

_____

_____

_____

_____

_____

_____

_____

_____

_____

_____

What is the main reason readers will care about my protagonist and feel tension due to caring what happens to him or her?

My answer: He will be an empathetic character due to being the victim of unfortunate circumstances (all those lightning strikes) and his personality, which is honorable, honest, self-sacrificing, generous, concerned for others, desirous of justice. As they watch him struggle with his past, his guilt, his fears, and his powers, they will want to see him conquer and find that inner peace. They will be able to relate to his emotional struggles and want to see him happy in the end.

Your answer:

_____

_____

_____

_____

_____

_____

_____

_____

What are the high stakes for my protagonist? What does he care most about and what is he willing to lose to reach his goal? Why will this create tension in the story?

My answer: The high stakes are his life and the lives of those at risk and depending on him to save them. He cares most about stopping the killer and saving lives and so is willing to die to do so. This will create tension as the story unfolds and shows the big danger lightning poses, to not just him (physically and spiritually/emotionally) but to the other characters that are put in danger by this big man vs. nature confrontation. Seeing the way hero struggles and the tough choices he has to make that require selflessness and self-sacrifice, readers will feel tense for him.

Your answer:

_____

_____

_____

_____

_____

_____

_____

Infusing Your Novel with Microtension

Writers also need to focus on microtension—which means every page of your novel should have a small, tight sense of tension seeping from the writing. Some of this pertains to writing mechanics (using phrasing and words that intrigue, add mystery, evoke imagery), but it primarily has to do with keeping the inner and outer conflict heightened at all times.

For example, anytime a character has conflicting feelings, you have microtension. Microtension can be small, simmering, subtext, subtle. Even the choice of words or the turn of a phrase can produce microtension by its freshness or unexpected usage.

A sudden change in emotion can create tension. A character struggling between two opposite emotions creates tension. Odd contradictory emotions and reactions can create microtension.

Microtension can be generated in three primary ways: through dialog, outer action, and exposition. Your inspection checklist will explore this more fully.

Inspection Checklist #8

Tension Ramped to the Max

Here are the sets of questions and exercises on your inspection checklist, and more. Take time to think these through and answer them. If you haven't yet come up with the solid answers you need for some of these questions, leave them blank and come back to them later.

Question Set #1:

What is the central *inner* conflict your protagonist is dealing with as it pertains to your concept?

_____

_____

_____

_____

_____

How can you increase that?

_____

_____

_____

_____

_____

Question Set #2:

Choose a random scene. What is the key outer conflict? Inner conflict?

_____

_____

_____

_____

How can you make each more complex in that scene?

_____

_____

_____

_____

_____

Make the character(s) more conflicted internally? Externally?

_____

_____

_____

_____

_____

Find time to do this examination with every scene in your novel.

Question Set #3:

Can you find a moment for your main characters to want the opposite of her heart's desire? What would that look like?

_____

_____

_____

_____

_____

_____

How might you do the same with your most important secondary character? Your nemesis character?

_____

_____

_____

_____

_____

_____

_____

_____

_____

_____

Question Set #4:

Go through your dialog in a random scene that has characters in conversation. In what ways can you add subtext and mystery?

_____

_____

_____

_____

_____

_____

_____

Go through and tighten the dialog. What things have you done to make the dialog more tense?

_____

_____

_____

_____

_____

_____

Find all your scenes that have dialog and spend time reworking to tighten and add subtext, mystery, and microtension. Work on random chapters out of order for the best results.

Question Set #5:

Print out your novel and toss the pages. Pick up ten pages. Can you find five places on each page in which to add microtension? What did you come up with? Repeat this each day you sit down to work on your novel.

_____

_____

_____

_____

_____

_____

_____

_____

_____

Question #6:

Go through your dialog in a random scene that has characters in conversation. Can you have characters say something other than what they mean (subtext)? Hint at something secret? List some ways:

_____

_____

_____

_____

_____

Question #7:

Can you add five places in your novel where a character could act rashly, inconsistently, or contrary? List them and explain how you will do this:

_____

_____

_____

_____

_____

_____

_____

Question #8:

Can you add at least one moment in five scenes when a character thinks, reacts, or does something wholly unexpected? List them and explain how you will do this:

_____

_____

_____

_____

_____

_____

_____

Question #9:

Look for high-action passages where tension should be high. Are the sentences short, packed with strong words, and showing strong emotion? Rewrite a sluggish passage so it zings with tension:

_____

_____

_____

_____

_____

_____

_____

_____

Question #10:

Find your lowest-tension scene. How can you make your protagonist more conflicted emotionally to ramp up the tension?

_____

_____

_____

_____

_____

Do this with all your low-tension scenes.

Question #11:

Do you have any scenes in which everyone is happy and all is well? What monkey wrench you can throw in to upend things?

_____

_____

_____

_____

_____

_____

_____

Question #12:

Have you gone through your latest draft to eliminate extraneous, boring, flat words and phrasing? If not, do so! Make a list of your "repeated offender" words—blah words you use too often—and give some better replacements:

_____

_____

_____

_____

_____

_____

_____

_____

_____

_____

_____

_____

_____

Write a one-paragraph summary of your novel highlighting Tension Ramped to the Max:

_____

_____

_____

_____

_____

_____

_____

_____

> ***Additional Exercise:*** Grab a few of your favorite novels. Open each book to random pages, then read each page and search for phrases or sentences that are full of tension. Look for microtension in dialog, action description, subtext, and exposition. What lines create curiosity or show inner conflict? Jot down your observations in a notebook, and see if you can apply similar technique in your scenes.

My Mind Map to Generate Tension Ramped to the Max

Primary sources of tension

From main plot with killer on The run + The ramping up of danger and stakes as people are hurt, killed, + kidnapped

From The outer + inner conflict of hero vs. lightning as danger increases The more he challenges The lightning. Tension (outer) from natural disasters That occur as a result of his powers going haywire + storm grows.

Readers' tension

→ Tension ← created by kicker:

They will care for hero as he's set up to be very empathetic. They will care what happens to him + want him to reach his goals. They will see his struggle w/ guilt and want him to win over his fears + beat The lightning, but they won't know if he will succeed. When he goes to sacrifice his life They will understand his desperation.

caused by conflict between characters

father, coworker, girlfriend - all create inner tension for hero.

coworker also creates huge outer conflict + plot tension

readers will be tense watching hero deal with his increasing powers, his growing madness, + The lightning personification paranormal mystery elements

High tension w/stakes : Can't have much higher . Stakes - what is at risk for hero: his life + sanity. At risk for all others around him + even The city (if a bomb threat, for example) - will create lots of tension

Your Mind Map to Generate Tension Ramped to the Max

PILLAR #9: DIALOG—COMPRESSED AND ESSENTIAL

Dialog is the element that brings stories alive. Imagine reading an entire novel void of dialog. Trying to sustain a whole novel—or even a few consecutive scenes—without any dialog would be difficult, for that would mean your story would have to be conveyed by narrative and internal thoughts alone. So our ninth essential pillar of novel construction is all about dialog.

Although we want the dialog in our scenes—like every other component—to be believable and feel "natural," the tendency for many writers is to write boring dialog.

Just as everyday people and situations can be boring, so too can dialog. But, as I've said many times before, readers don't want "boring." They read to be entertained, inspired, excited, moved, changed.

Yet, we need a balance between boring and ridiculous. Dialog that is over-stylized, overly stiff, or unnatural is jarring. The key to "proper" dialog lies with the characters who are speaking.

Here are some basics on crafting great dialog:

- **Make sure it fits the context and the character**.

- **No one should sound like anyone else. Unless you have some funny bit about a character mimicking another character, each person should be unique.**

- **Don't use dialog to dump information.**

- **Don't tell us things we already know or don't care about. Many beginning writers make the mistake of needless repetition.**

Compressing Dialog

The trick to great dialog, as hinted at by the title of this pillar of novel construction, is to *compress* the dialog. Just what does that mean? Here are some ways:

- **Avoid "on the nose" dialog. This means that characters should never simply state exactly what's on their minds, without nuance or subtext, nor appear to be giving "exposition."**

- **Less is more. If you can "say" the same thing with a visual image, action, behavior, or sound effect instead of through dialog, omit the dialog. Trim out extra words, boring bits of info and phrasing.**

- **Have a specific purpose for what's being said, and lead steadily to your point. Don't have random chatting that serves no purpose.**

There is so much more to crafting great dialog, but this general overview should give you some things to consider.

Start going through your scenes and look at the dialog. Read it out loud. You'll hear the clunky, boring bits. Take those out. If you need to have characters introduced or say hello, just note that with a short line of narrative or dialog, then move on quickly to what it important in your scene.

First: Read chapter 23 in *The 12 Key Pillars of Novel Construction* that covers Pillar #9 before you start the hard work on Dialog—Compressed and Essential.

Brainstorm Key Questions

Spend some time brainstorming these questions meant to get you thinking about the dialog in your novel.

Who will my protagonist talk with most in the novel and why? What important elements of the plot will be brought out in these conversations?

My answer: He would talk mostly to himself and to the lightning. Through these one-sided dialogs a lot of the plot can be revealed. Much of his past (backstory) and his motivation would come through his conversations with his ally (lightning survivor). This will help hero make decisions that will move the plot forward as hero values his input.

Your answer:

_____

_____

_____

_____

_____

_____

What important backstory points will I reveal through dialog and by whom? In what scenes?

My answer: Hero will reveal his guilt over his past to his ally from the survivors' group in a key scene or two when hero needs help to make the right choices (to commit to his goal). In argument with Dad backstory about the accidental death will be revealed. His history with lightning and his special powers can come out in dialog with some team members, the killer, and/or his love interest close to the climax when it's now clear there are greater forces at work in the mountains as they confront the killer and the danger is at its peak (from the killer and from the natural elements).

Your answer:

_____

_____

_____

_____

_____

_____

_____

_____

_____

What character(s) might I have that adds humor or an intriguing style of speaking that will help create engaging dialog? Explain:

My answer: I think his main ally has to have the sense of humor. Even though he is disabled and in chronic pain, his attitude about life, his spirituality and faith in God and in the hero can be a source of comfort and encouragement to hero. He can have a crazy background and personality that lends toward humor.

Your answer:

_____

_____

_____

_____

_____

What conversation will be the most important in my novel? What will be revealed in it that is essential to the plot?

My answer: It has to be one near the climax when he's most despairing, with one of the team members (whoever hasn't been captured or killed), in which he confesses his greatest fears and guilt and the truth about the lightning, and shows his willingness to die.

Your answer:

_____

_____

_____

_____

_____

_____

Creating Engaging Dialog by Using Subtext

Just what is subtext? Subtext refers to the thoughts that the character is *not* saying—ideas that are being suggested but not actually voiced directly. They are below (sub) the text.

Real people use subtext constantly. We almost never really say what we mean or voice what we really want. We hide our feelings and cover with expressions and words that imply something other. We do this to protect ourselves, or to present a certain impression.

How might some of that dialog be shown in subtext? In other words, what does my protagonist or secondary character need to say but can't say outright? How does this reveal something he is afraid of?

My answer: Hero could avoid facing the truth of his guilt over his brother's death. He wouldn't talk to others directly about his relationship with lightning or his special powers. He wants to keep these secret, so he would talk in other terms. His friend would sense the

235

issues beneath the dialog and know how to help. Also lots of subtext in talking with his father, as his father blames hero for the brother's death and hero already believes and feels that from his father. His girlfriend could also confront him, wondering why he's acting crazy taking big risks, but he can't tell her the truth.

Your answer:

_____

_____

_____

_____

_____

_____

_____

Additional Exercise: Write a scene that has dialog, and have characters say outright what they want and mean. Then go through and change the wording so that they aren't saying those things. Have a character talk about something *other*, while your narrative is revealing she is trying to say something else. Show from your character's actions, facial expressions, and gestures that she is not saying what she really means. Skim some novels and find great dialog that uses subtext. Jot down notes on how the author did this.

Inspection Checklist #9

Dialog—Compressed and Essential

Here are the sets of questions and exercises on your inspection checklist, and more. Take time to think these through and answer them. If you haven't yet come up with the solid answers you need for some of these questions, leave them blank and come back to them later.

Question #1:

Go through all the dialog in your scenes. Have you tightened and trimmed to condense, removing all boring, mundane, and unimportant lines? What are some of the phrases you eliminated?

_____

_____

_____

_____

_____

Question #2:

Have you gone through and removed all unnecessary speaker tags? Conversely, have you made sure it's clear who is speaking? Once you have done so, mark this question completed.

_____

Question #3:

Have you made sure to alternate speaker tags with narrative bits to show both who is speaking and what the tone, mood, reaction, or emotion is? Once you have done so, mark this question completed.

Question #4:

Have you made sure each line of dialog well reflects each character's personality, background, education, and ethnicity? Once you have done so, mark this question completed.

Question #5:

Have you checked to ensure none of your dialog is used as an info dump, telling readers or characters what they already know? Once you have done so, mark this question completed.

Question #6:

Have you removed or changed all "on the nose" dialog—characters saying exactly what they are feeling? Replaced with subtext and implication? Once you have done so, mark this question completed.

Question #7:

Have you removed all adverbs in speaker tags and instead found a way to *show* the emotion of the character as she speaks? Once you have done so, mark this question completed.

Question #8:

Does every spoken line in your scenes serve a purpose? Help to reveal character or a new plot development? If not, change or take it out. Once you have done so, mark this question completed.

Question #9:

Have you found places where you can insert moments of silence to add tension? Find some more. Once you have done so, mark this question completed.

Question #10:

Have you checked to make sure each character's speech and actions are grouped together in paragraphs to make clear who is speaking? Once you have done so, mark this question completed.

Question #11:

Have you gone through and removed excessive "flowery" speaker tag verbs such as cajoled, postulated, and elucidated? Once you have done so, mark this question completed.

Question #12:

Have you checked to make sure your characters speak naturally, using contractions where needed? Once you have done so, mark this question completed.

Additional Exercise: Grab a few novels. Find passages of dialog that you feel show great tension. Examine why the dialog is gripping. Look for subtext, tight writing. Conversely, see if you can spot any "on the nose" dialog, excessive adverbs or speaker tags, or clunky speech. Think how you would rewrite the dialog so it's tighter and more tense and interesting.

PILLAR #10: VOICE—UNIQUE FOR EACH CHARACTER

Each character in your novel has his or her own voice, whether a child, a man or woman, a dog, or a robot. Every POV character in your novel has a unique voice—both internally, in the way he thinks, as well as in his audible speech.

In addition, any character that speaks out loud (not a POV character) has a voice as well. A POV character might be mute, but she would still have a voice because the reader can hear what she is thinking in her head.

Voice pertains to the manner, style, and presentation of that speech. With non-POV characters, their voice comes out only in the words they actually say and how they're said—since the writer is not going into their heads.

With POV characters, voice embodies more than spoken words or direct thoughts in their heads. The narrative should reflect that voice as well. When you craft a scene in a character's POV, every line in that scene has to feel as though it is being processed, chewed, and spit out by that character. Everything that happens in that scene is witnessed, experienced, felt, and reacted to by that character. And so, even the narrative must have "voice."

A six-year-old should sound her age and not sound like an adult. In addition, where she lives and how she is being raised will affect the words she uses and the things she notices and thinks about.

If you think of voice as just an extension of dialog—as the POV character speaking through the entire narrative of the scene—it may help you to get a handle on voice.

First: Read chapter 24 in *The 12 Key Pillars of Novel Construction* that covers Pillar #10 before you start the hard work on Voice—Unique for Each Character.

Brainstorm Key Questions

Spend some time brainstorming these questions meant to get you thinking about voice in your novel. Each character needs a unique voice, one that fits just right.

What unique voice have I given to my protagonist? How does his background, upbringing, education, and self-image affect his voice?

My answer: He's an educated, intellectual man who's gone to college and studied science, including some physics, botany, forestry, zoology, so his voice will reflect his education. But he's a no-nonsense guy and totally unpretentious, so he's not going to use big words or try to impress. He's straightforward and honest, gets to the point, doesn't have a haughty opinion of himself. He was raised in a city (perhaps Denver or Seattle) so that will influence the scope of his thinking and voice.

Your answer:

_____

_____

_____

_____

_____

_____

What unique voice have I given to my important secondary characters? How do backgrounds, upbringing, education, and self-image factor into their voices?

My answer: I'd like his humorous ally male friend to be from the South (where all that lightning strikes), and a down-home kind of guy with a strong Southern style and manner of voice. His girlfriend will be more uptight class-conscious, ambitious city girl (maybe originally from East Coast?) with clipped speech, short snappy dialog. The antagonist coworker who is a pain will be (sorry) a total redneck from some rural town that is close-minded, poorly educated but tries to imply he knows everything. His arrogance and stupidity will be apparent in his voice.

Your answer:

_____

_____

_____

_____

_____

_____

_____

_____

What stands out most about my main character's voice? Why?

My answer: *His deep thinking and thoughtful consideration of everything he sees, feels, and experiences. He is on a big self-discovery mission in order to find peace and sanity, so his voice will reflect his seriousness and manner of tearing at everything for understanding, knowledge, and insight.*

Your answer:

_____

_____

_____

_____

_____

_____

Additional Exercise: Grab a few novels you love and take a look at the voice of the characters. First, choose a novel with a first-person POV. Jot down a list of ten qualities of that character's voice. Is she snarky, confident, whiny, erudite, ignorant? Look at novels that use third-person POV and do the same with a few characters from each book. What ideas do you pick up about crafting a strong, unique voice for your characters?

Inspection Checklist #10

Voice—Unique for Each Character

Here are the sets of questions and exercises on your inspection checklist, and more. Take time to think these through and answer them. If you haven't yet come up with the solid answers you need for some of these questions, leave them blank and come back to them later.

Question #1:

Have you thoroughly developed all your characters and created a speaking style for them? Once done, mark this question completed.

Question #2:

Have you thoroughly developed all your POV characters and created a narrative voice style? Once done, mark this question completed.

Question #3:

Have you checked to make sure each character's speaking voice and POV narrative voice sound similar in all your scenes? Once you have done so, mark this question completed.

Question #4:

Have you checked to ensure the voices for your POV characters are correct for their age, and that this is reflected in the narrative? Once you have done so, mark this question completed.

_____

Question Set #5:

Think about each character's "word whiskers" or special phrases. What are some of the things they repeatedly say? List the character and his/her pet words or phrases:

_____

_____

_____

_____

_____

_____

_____

_____

_____

_____

_____

_____

Have you pulled those into the POV narrative in appropriate places? Once you have done so, mark this question completed.

Question #6:

Does the narrative of each scene reflect and reveal the *mind-set or attitude* of the POV character? Once you have done so, mark this question completed.

Question #7:

Does the narrative of each scene reflect and reveal the *mood and emotion* of the POV character? Once you have done so, mark this question completed.

Question #8:

Is your POV narrative voice void of vocabulary that your character would not use in his thoughts or speech? Once you have checked all your scenes, mark this question completed.

Question #9:

For your POV characters: How is their speech shaped by where they grew up, their education, ethnicity, and status? Explain in what way:

_____

_____

_____

_____

_____

_____

_____

Question #10:

If you are writing in first-person POV, what are some ways you have made this a unique and compelling voice?

_____

_____

_____

_____

_____

_____

Question #11:

Have you checked through all your scenes to make sure there is no author intrusion—narrating "out of POV"? Once you have done so, mark this question completed.

Question #12:

If you are writing in omniscient voice, have you developed a unique narrative voice that feels like a character in your book? Is this voice strong and present in every scene? Once you have checked all your scenes, mark this question completed.

Write a one-paragraph summary of your novel highlighting Voice Unique for Each Character:

_____

_____

_____

_____

_____

_____

_____

PILLAR #11: WRITING STYLE—CONCISE AND SPECIFIC

Writing style is an important pillar of novel construction for it is the way you tell your story. You've learned that "voice" is all about characters, whereas writing style is about how writers present the story in all its components. The choices a writer makes as to scene structure and style; length of sentences, paragraphs, and chapters; and the sophistication (or not) of vocabulary and word choice and literary devices (such as metaphor, similes, anaphora) comes under the "heading" of writing style.

A novel's style needs to be both concise and specific. In what ways? The first consideration when deciding upon a writing style is audience. Whom are you writing this book for? What genre is it? Readers of genres have certain expectations when it comes to writing style, so being specific involves making sure your style is characteristic of the genre.

Concise writing involves mechanics. *Concise* means "brevity of expression or statement; free from all elaboration and superfluous detail," says *Merriam-Webster's Collegiate Dictionary*. Some synonyms are *terse, succinct, laconic, summary, pithy, compendious.* As I often declare: "Say what you mean. Don't say what you don't mean." Choose your words carefully and make them count.

Don't belabor these details in your first draft; just get the writing on the page. But when you begin fine-tuning during your revisions, take the time to cut down clunky writing, choose stronger nouns and verbs, and eliminate repetition. Invest in your career as a writer by learning to wield language in a concise, effective way.

First: Read chapter 25 in *The 12 Key Pillars of Novel Construction* that covers Pillar #11 before you start the hard work on Writing Style—Concise and Specific.

Brainstorm Key Questions

Spend some time brainstorming these questions meant to get you thinking about your writing style. Your style needs to be specific—meaning it should be deliberate and appropriate for the genre, tone you mean to set, and the plot you are telling. It also needs to be concise—say what you mean. Don't say what you don't mean.

Who are your favorite authors that write books similar to yours? What is it about their writing style that you enjoy, and what characteristics about their writing do you want to emulate?

My answer: Kathryn Magendie's *The Lightning Charmer* (paranormal romance) has great creative, magical style in the writing. It's a blend of imaginative with practical. I want this book to fall in the genre of paranormal suspense, but with more a commercial suspense feel. So I'll aim for a style similar to authors like Heather Graham and Allison Brennan.

Your answer:

_____

_____

_____

_____

_____

How do you feel about the story you are writing? What emotions are sparked by your plot and concept, and what are you hoping readers will feel when they've read your novel?

My answer: I'm excited about the inner conflict process of my protagonist and the heavy emotions he will deal with, especially the guilt/shame and his journey to surrender. I'd like readers to really relate to this emotional journey and feel they've gained personal insight about these things in their own lives.

Your answer:

_____

_____

_____

_____

_____

_____

What kind of a tone do you want to convey in your novel and why?

My answer: Overall suspenseful, not too dark, which could easily happen with all the elements of this story. So the heavy contemplative and dark moments of action need to be balanced with some humor and upbeat moments as well.

Your answer:

_____

_____

_____

_____

_____

_____

_____

How much author presence do you want to have come through the narrative? Explain why this may or may not be appropriate.

My answer: I don't want any author presence. I just want to show this story play out and let readers be fully in the minds of the characters.

Your answer:

_____

_____

_____

_____

_____

_____

What do you feel are your weaknesses regarding the writing style you hope to use for this novel? How will you work on them?

My answer: Figuring out how to do a good blend of straight suspense style with adding a more creative flair to infuse the story with intriguing paranormal elements. I will study some novels in the paranormal suspense genre to get ideas for this genre.

Your answer:

_____

_____

_____

_____

> *Additional Exercise:* You should be reading loads of books in your genre to get a feel for the types of writing styles successful authors use. But stop and take the time to jot down a list of what some of those attributes are. Do these authors write in short, crisp sentences? Do they feature a lot of fast-moving dialog? How sophisticated is the vocabulary and sentence structure? How creative do they get with their prose? By seeing what these authors do in common, you will get some good ideas of what type of writing style you need.

Inspection Checklist #11

Writing Style—Concise and Specific

Here are the sets of questions and exercises on your inspection checklist, and more. Take time to think these through and answer them. If you haven't yet come up with the solid answers you need for some of these questions, leave them blank and come back to them later.

Question #1:

Have you gone through your scenes to ensure the characters' narrative voices are different from your "writer's" voice? Once done, mark this question completed.

_____

Question #2:

What genre are you writing in? Have you studied numerous novels in your genre to "get" the range of writing styles that are appropriate? Describe some of the style elements that factor into a writing style for this genre:

_____

_____

_____

_____

_____

Question #3:

Have you done a search through your novel for your weasel words and removed or replaced with stronger words? Once done, mark this question completed.

Question #4:

Have you done a search for weak construction, such as *ly* and *ing* to find passive voice and adverbs that may be causing clunky writing? Once done, mark this question completed.

Question #5:

Have you gone through every sentence to make sure you've chosen the best, most appropriate words to convey your intended meaning? Once done, mark this question completed.

Question #6:

Can you find passages you sense are forced, pretentious, or fake? Try freewriting new passages with simple, honest intent. Any better? Once done, mark this question completed.

Question #7:

Read through your scenes and pay attention to how your body feels. Do any passages feel "wrong" to you? If so, try rewriting until they feel right. Once done, mark this question completed.

_____

Question Set #8:

Do you spend time reading great novels? Who are your favorite authors in your genre?

_____

_____

_____

Are you taking time to read to inspire your writing? Set up a regular reading schedule to do this. When you've got it in your calendar and you're keeping faithful to your schedule, mark this question completed.

_____

Question Set #9:

What type of tone is best for your book?

_____

_____

Have you gone through your scenes to bring out that tone through all the narrative? Once done, mark this question completed.

_____

Question Set #10:

Have you thought about how much or little you want your "writing voice" to come through your narrative? What's best for your genre?

_____

_____

_____

Question #11:

Do you struggle with grammar? If so, have you committed to buying some books and/or taking classes to improve? If you've done so and you're applying yourself, mark this question completed.

_____

Question Set #12:

Have you given yourself permission to "let yourself go" and experiment with your writing style? If yes, mark this question completed.

_____

What is your biggest weakness with your writing style? What needs attention and improvement?

_____

_____

_____

_____

_____

_____

_____

Make time to work intensely on this problem until you are satisfied you are conquering it!

Write a one-paragraph summary of your novel highlighting Writing Style—Concise and Specific:

_____

_____

_____

_____

_____

_____

_____

PILLAR #12: MOTIFS FOR COHESION AND DEPTH

Not every novel in every genre needs to contain a motif (or two or five), but motifs can supercharge your story, and it's very likely that if you add some, you can make your novel more interesting and memorable.

Novels that present powerful motifs reach readers on multiple levels, for we humans resonate with symbols, and although a motif isn't strictly (or always) a symbol of some sort, a motif carries symbolic import to some extent.

Theme is what your book is "really about." But a theme is not a motif. Motifs are symbolic elements packed with inference. Motifs can be a "thing"—some object that makes a repeated appearance in your novel. Or they can be word or phrase, a concept, an image—just about anything that can be repeated with significance and symbolism. The weather can be a motif, for example, if each time something terrible is about to happen, "lightning" strikes (and you've been seeing how lightning works as a motif in my example story idea).

Motifs are powerful elements that writers can take advantage of when constructing their novels. But few novelists ever give thought to adding motifs. They might do so subconsciously or inadvertently, but I'd like to encourage you to take some time and deliberately construct some motifs so that they serve as Superglue in your story.

First: Read chapter 26 in *The 12 Key Pillars of Novel Construction* that covers Pillar #12 before you start the hard work on Motifs for Cohesion and Depth.

Brainstorm Key Questions

Spend some time brainstorming these questions meant to get you thinking about the motifs in your novel.

The best way to bring a motif into your story is to tie it intrinsically into your theme. Once you work to develop the themes in your novel, you can create some motifs.

Think for a moment about your theme, what your story is *really* about. What images come to mind that might represent your novel?

My answer: Lightning is the strongest motif element in the story. The themes of enlightenment—my hero needing to find the light of truth—can tie in great with lightning as a symbol of illumination and stark truth. Truth can be painful and stab or shock like lightning. Lightning is powerful and can start wildfires, which can be both literal and emotional in the story.

Your answer:

_____

_____

_____

_____

_____

_____

What key moment in your entire story would best be shown on your movie poster? What colors and objects would be shown? What would the characters be wearing, holding, doing?

My answer: My poster would show my character atop the mountain peak facing the lightning, with the killer and lookout tower in the background. Colors would be dark and stormy in contrast to the bright flash of lightning. Hero's fist would be shaking at the sky, and he'd be in his park uniform. Other characters could be held captive by the cabin or not there at all.

My title should be something like *The Lightning Man.*

Your answer:

_____

_____

_____

_____

_____

_____

_____

_____

_____

_____

Think about your protagonist. Imagine one object he owns that is special to him. What is it, and why is it significant?

My answer: Some object from his past that connects to his dead brother that was melted from the lightning. It could be a toy that had belonged to his brother. It brings him pain to carry it but he needs that reminder of his guilt. Or it could be something his ally gives him to give him strength and courage. Something that survived unscathed when the ally got struck by lightning, that he feels is a good-luck charm.

Your answer:

_____

_____

_____

_____

_____

_____

_____

_____

_____

_____

Take that object and turn it into a symbol of some sort for your protagonist. What emotions or thoughts does it evoke for him?

My answer: In addition to getting him to think about his guilt and/or his need for strength and courage to face his past and fears, it should somehow symbolize his destiny and his search for truth. Maybe a key would be good because of the symbolism connected with that—keys open doors (to knowledge and awareness). He might feel that the key to all his answers is there somewhere, but like the melted key, it can't fit in the lock. Whatever object he relates to, he should always carry it with him superstitiously and gets upset if others ask about it or belittle his attitude about it.

Your answer:

_____

_____

_____

_____

_____

_____

_____

How can you reinforce the motif by finding other ways and places to put it in your story?

My answer: If using a key, there could be other keys. The keys to his house (that he may be losing), keys to his father's house (that make him think how to get back into his father's heart). With the lightning motif, he could have a saying about lightning strikes that has deep significance to him, that he shares with ally.

Your answer:

_____

_____

_____

_____

_____

_____

Additional Exercise: Pull out a sheet of paper and write down an emotion or thematic component from your novel, such as grief or justice, then list all the words, objects, and images that come to your mind. Picture your character feeling or thinking about these things. Where is she? What does she see, touch, hold? Grab some of these things and find ways to put them in your scenes in a significant way.

Inspection Checklist #12

Motifs for Cohesion and Depth

Here are the sets of questions and exercises on your inspection checklist, and more. Take time to think these through and answer them. If you haven't yet come up with the solid answers you need for some of these questions, leave them blank and come back to them later.

Question #1:

What are 3-4 motifs you can come up with for your novel that will tie in with your theme? Describe them in detail.

_____

_____

_____

_____

_____

_____

_____

_____

_____

_____

Question #2:

Can you think of an object/item from your protagonist's past that is emotionally charged? List three ideas of how and in what ways you can bring that object into a scene as a motif:

_____

_____

_____

_____

_____

_____

_____

_____

_____

Question #3:

Can you think of a symbol that has some universal (or common) meaning that can become significant for your protagonist? Explain:

_____

_____

_____

_____

_____

Question Set #4:

Have you created an image system for your novel? Describe it, and include words, colors, phrases, objects. How will you bring these items into your story?

_____

_____

_____

_____

_____

_____

_____

_____

Question Set #5:

Picture your movie poster for your novel. What important objects and setting stand out? Where and in what ways will they fit into your novel?

_____

_____

_____

_____

Question Set #6:

Think of the main emotion or trait your protagonist experiences (grief, forgiveness, etc.). Can you find a symbol/object for this to use in your novel? What key scenes will use this?

_____

_____

_____

_____

_____

_____

_____

_____

_____

Question #7

What phrase or sentences can an ally character say to your protagonist that can be repeated as motif?

_____

_____

_____

_____

_____

Question Set #8

Consider the title of your novel. Can you find a way to bring a motif into the title? Tie in with your themes? Play with some ideas:

_____

_____

_____

_____

_____

_____

Question #9

Think of the main themes of your story, then freewrite word associations of emotions, objects, or images. Can you use some of these for motifs in your story? Where?

_____

_____

_____

_____

_____

_____

_____

_____

Question Set #10

What comforts your character the most? A song, phrase, object, person? Where in your novel will you use this as a motif in your book?

_____

_____

_____

_____

_____

_____

_____

Question #11

Describe the three most important scenes in your novel for your protagonist. How can you insert the same motif into those three scenes somehow?

_____

_____

_____

_____

_____

_____

_____

_____

_____

_____

Question #12

When you're finished with your novel, what motif can you bring out in both the first scene and the last (with your protagonist) that features your main motif?

_____

_____

_____

_____

_____

Write a one-paragraph summary of your novel highlighting Motifs for Cohesion and Depth:

_____

_____

_____

_____

_____

My Mind Map to Generate Motifs for Cohesion and Depth

Lightning

great motif + symbol
- of truth, clarity
- sudden understanding, enlightenment
- power, electricity - very empowering

Find some sayings or quotes about lightning that can be used in survivors' group + serve as motif in book

Shines light on truth. Can literally illuminate the setting to help hero spot the killer at one point

Play with lightning/light similarities

Something to symbolize his fear? guilt?

Motifs

Something his brother gave him or used to belong to him -
- symbolizes their love, companionship, loyalty
- reminds hero of the bond they had
- a stone/gem they found? quartz crystal
- can symbolize purity, clarity?
- or a phrase he used to say?
  - Be a light in the darkness or light chases scary shadows away?

what could oppose lightning - be a good memory object that gives him strength?
- something he carried or wore that saved him when struck by lightning?

- something he found in the mountains that had survived lightning?

a piece of burnt wood that lightning etched a symbol in - that looks like a word/object?

Something his ally at the meetings gives to him
- an object like a key that melted in his pocket when he got struck by lightning -
- uses it for hero to symbolize
  - hope
  - courage to "open" the door to truth
- tie in with key Ben Franklin had on end of string to catch lightning
- use "key" motive on many levels. Maybe hero holds it up to lightning at climax?

Your Mind Map to Generate Motifs for Cohesion and Depth

3

ADDITIONAL MIND MAPS YOU CAN CREATE

In addition to the basic pillar mind maps you've created, you can work on other aspects of your novel, or even combine mind maps. Work through tough problems you are having with your plot and subplots, characters, and other components. If, after you've gone through all the pillar exercises in this workbook as well as the inspection checklists, and you have some blank sections you just can't figure out, consider mind mapping those questions to get the answers you need.

Let your imagination flow as you come up with ideas, and don't censor yourself.

Here are some mind maps you can create that might help you further:

- *Characters and themes*: You want your protagonist to embody or showcase your themes, but your secondary characters can also do so.

  - ○ Think about setting characters in opposition regarding thematic elements for a great source of conflict (which you know, by now, is a good thing).

  - ○ Note what each character is passionate about and how this ties into theme. You may have done mind maps for developing your themes, your protagonist and goal, and your secondary characters, but play around with combining these elements in one mind map.

  - ○ Next to each character, note what aspects of his background, past, or upbringing might contribute to why he feels strongly about your theme(s).

- o Think about possible scene ideas as you work on this map.

- *Conflict and high stakes with your protagonist and secondary characters*:

  - o Look over your mind map for your protagonist with a goal and the one for your secondary characters. Create a mind map that puts them all together, then play with the stakes for each character and see how you can make them as high as possible.

  - o Find ways to interconnect these characters' stakes and amplify them. Come up with scene ideas that could show how one character's goal and its stakes impacts another. For example, a man might get fired from his job due to helping the protagonist. As a result, his wife might leave him and take the kids. He might get hurt in a car accident rushing off to find them.

  - o Make a list on the map of every possible awful complication, setback, disaster you could have happen in your story (that fits well into your plot). Then draw lines connecting each complication to a particular character as a possible plot complication for the story.

  - o Generate scene ideas, highlighting the main point of each with emphasis on how the stakes are now raised. I'll put a star next to the scenes I know I'll use, so when I start creating a scene outline (or put them on index cards), I'll know which ones to grab.

  - o Reversals are great plot twists. Think how every bad event in your story might have some residual good effect (such as disaster bringing the love interests together). Conversely, consider how each great step forward for a character might create an awful repercussion (such as a character finding an important clue to a kidnapping, only to learn it's his fault his child was taken).

- *Characters and settings*: Settings are important not just for your protagonist but also your secondary characters. Take a look at your settings mind map alongside your secondary characters one. See if you can interconnect these so that more characters can interact with the same settings.

    o Think of one important past event in the life of each character that links them emotionally to a place and that influenced how they view the world and themselves.

    o Come up with scene ideas at these specific locales that involve more than one main character. Think how to make the scene more emotionally charged due to the memories the place evokes.

- *Mind map your weak components.* After answering the questions to all your twelve inspection checklists, you may be aware of specific aspects of your novel that are weak. Often this turns out being shallow undeveloped characters, uninteresting or unimportant plot or subplot threads, or boring settings that don't have meaning for your characters or help enhance the novel. Find those tough questions you couldn't answer confidently and create a mind map just for those.

    If you allow yourself to brainstorm ideas without censoring, by jotting down whatever comes to your mind, however crazy, you will probably come up with exactly what you need. Writer's block at the idea stage can be broken through by action—putting pen to paper and knocking down the walls of criticism. You know you can just throw your chart out—no commitments, no intimidation. And often, in the process, you'll generate many cool ideas for other novels that you can stick in your notebook and get to later—after you finish writing this killer novel!

I hope you discover how mind mapping and brainstorming your ideas for all your twelve key pillars of novel construction will aid you to build super-strong supports for the weight of your story!

ADDITIONAL MIND MAPS

ADDITIONAL MIND MAPS

ADDITIONAL MIND MAPS

ADDITIONAL MIND MAPS

ADDITIONAL MIND MAPS

ADDITIONAL MIND MAPS

CONCLUSION

Novel writing is not an easy venture. As you've seen, writers need to truly understand structure to build a great story. By following this blueprint of building the four foundational corner pillars first and making sure they are solid, you can prevent wasting weeks, months, or years of your life writing a novel that just won't hold up.

With a solid concept and unique kicker, an empathetic protagonist who is passionately pursuing a meaningful (for him) goal, a story drenched in conflict and high stakes that showcases universal issues (theme) that readers all over the world, in any era, would care about, your novel will stand strong, rising above the hundreds of thousands of novels built on sand or out of faulty materials.

Working hard in advance to ensure a strong structure does not take the joy out of creativity or curtail a writer in any way. Quite the opposite is true. Within framework is the freedom to be confidently expressive.

One of my favorite movies comes to mind when I think about novel structure: *The Legend of 1900*. This beautiful story stretching over decades tells about a baby born in 1900 on a cruise ship who is abandoned by an unknown mother, is raised by workers on the ship, and learns to play the piano. This amazing prodigy, however, never steps foot off this ship his entire life. He just can't muster the courage to leave, so he spends his life traversing the Atlantic Ocean, playing in the big band and astounding listeners with his musical talent.

One of the greatest scenes in this movie is when this young man, Danny (also known as 1900) explains to his best friend, Max, why he just can't leave the ship. He says the world is too big, that it doesn't have any boundaries; it has no end. He can't live with such vast possibilities. He needed to define his life "between prow and stern." Land was "a ship too big" for him.

Danny says, "The keys are not infinite. You are infinite. And on those keys, the music that you can make is infinite. . . . But if that keyboard had millions of keys . . . if it was infinite, then on that keyboard there is no music you can play."

Within that framework of eighty-eight keys, a pianist can create a limitless number of pieces, beautiful creations of endless variety. The framework isn't a limitation; it's an opportunity. He adds, "It is life."

And so too, within the framework of expected novel structure, any great idea can come to life. The possibilities are infinite for amazing stories.

You just have to build them—one pillar at a time.

C. S. Lakin
March, 2015

ABOUT THE AUTHOR

C. S. Lakin is a multipublished award-winning novelist and writing coach who loves to help writers find joy and success in their novel-writing journey. She works full-time as a copyeditor (fiction and nonfiction) and critiques about two hundred manuscripts a year. She teaches writing workshops around the country and gives instruction on her award-winning blog **Live Write Thrive** (www.livewritethrive.com). For manuscript critiques, visit Lakin's critique website **Critique My Manuscript** (critiquemymanuscript.com).

Lakin lives in a small town south of San Francisco, CA, with her husband Lee, a gigantic lab named Coaltrane, and three persnickety cats. She loves to hike and backpack, cook, watch basketball, and spend time with her two daughters and grandson.

Did you find this writing craft book helpful? The best way to thank a writer is to leave a positive, honest review. Be sure to leave a review for this book online that will help other writers learn how to construct a solid, enduring story!

Want to become the best novelist you can be?

The Writer's Toolbox series will give you all the tools you need to write terrific, well-structured stories that will stand the test of time and scrutiny.

- ***Say What? The Fiction Writer's Handy Guide to Grammar, Punctuation, and Word Usage*** is designed to help writers get a painless grasp on grammar. *Available in print and ebook on all online venues.*

- ***Writing the Heart of Your Story: The Secret to Crafting an Unforgettable Novel*** will teach you how to mine the heart of your plot, characters, themes, and so much more. If you want to write a book that targets the heart of readers, you need to know the heart of your story. *Available in print and ebook on all online venues.*

- ***Shoot Your Novel: Cinematic Techniques to Supercharge Your Writing***—an essential writing craft guide that will teach you the art of "show, don't tell" using time-tested cinematic technique. In this era of visual media, readers want more than ever to "see" stories unfold before their eyes. By utilizing film technique and adapting the various camera shots into your fiction, your writing will undergo a stunning transformation from "telling" to "showing."

59166089R00163

Made in the USA
Middletown, DE
10 August 2019